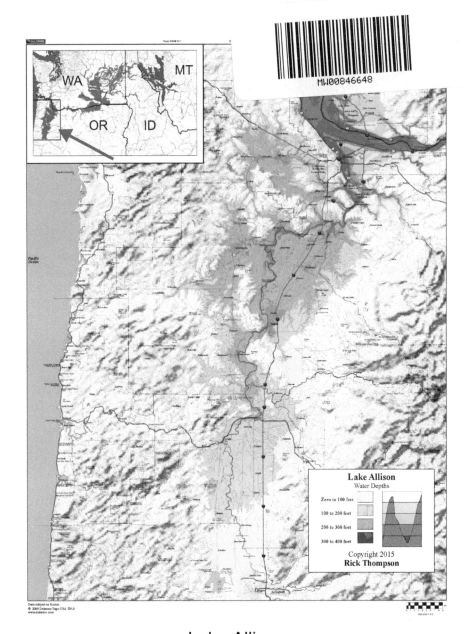

Lake Allison
Water Depths

Zero to 100 feet

100 to 200 feet

200 to 300 feet

300 to 400 feet

Copyright 2015
Rick Thompson

Lake Allison
In Oregon's Willamette Valley
during the largest Lake Missoula Flood
the "GigaFlood"

(Map by Rick Thompson)

GigaFlood

The Largest of the
Lake Missoula Floods
In Northwest Oregon
and
Southwest Washington

Revised Second Edition

Revised Second Edition

Copyright © 2015 Rick Thompson

Printed in the United States
Published by **LMF Publishing**

Cover photograph: Willamette Falls, Rick Thompson
Cover design: Rick Thompson

ISBN 978-0-9890840-2-4

LMF Publishing
P.O. Box 33056
Portland, OR 97292

GigaFlood

The Largest of the
Lake Missoula Floods
In Northwest Oregon
and
Southwest Washington

Revised Second Edition

by
Rick Thompson

LMF Publishing
Portland, OR

Table of Contents

Foreword

This good book tells the fantastic story of what happened in Portland when the great Glacial Lake Missoula floods washed down the Columbia River, and backed up into the Willamette Valley.

Canadian ice moving south passed Sandpoint dammed the Clark Fork River to impound Glacial Lake Missoula. Water rose behind that ice dam year by year as it flooded the mountain valleys of western Montana. The inevitable end came when the water got deep enough to float the ice dam, which then washed out and dumped Glacial Lake Missoula onto eastern Washington. That may have involved as much as 500 cubic miles of water, and may have happened as many as several dozen times.

The flood was as much as 1,000 feet deep in the Columbia Gorge, and must have arrived in the Portland basin as a wall of very fast water hundreds of feet high. That water slammed hard against the rock wall of the Tualatin Mountains, and poured south through the valleys of the Willamette and Tualatin Rivers into the Willamette Valley, which it flooded as far south as Eugene.

All that watery chaos left the Portland area richly supplied with evidence of its passing, all laid out for everyone to see. It told a wonderful story of one of the most dramatic and complex events of the last great ice age. Urban development during the last century destroyed much of that evidence, and hid much of the rest from easy public view. Hardly a week passes without some of the flood sculptured land falling victim to bulldozers and paving projects.

Boulders dropped from melting icebergs tell a vivid story of the great floods that carried them from distant sources, then dropped them where we now see them, strangers among us. Using these traveled boulders as mere landscape rocks strips them of their special meaning, leaving them as just another bunch of dumb rocks.

Rick Thompson has done a wonderful job of pointing out much of what remains of the wealth of evidence the great floods left strewn so lavishly across the Portland area. He shows us the best of what remains.

This book is a marvelous gift to the people of Portland. It will gain in value as the passing years bring more destruction. I hope it may help save some of what remains.

Dave Alt, Ph.D.
Professor Emeritus of Geology
University of Montana

Preface

As a native Oregonian, I have always been fascinated with the landscape around me. After a visit to eastern Washington, where the Lake Missoula flood evidence is so dramatic in expansive views, I began to wonder how it had affected where I live in Portland. But on this subject it was as if anything past the west end of the Columbia River Gorge was terra incognita – the unknown lands. I had to find out. It was a mystery I had to solve.

Taking on the challenge and encouraged by others, I embarked on a journey for over 20 years researching to find the many subtle hydrologic and geologic features of this neglected region that eluded public awareness. And I found a flood of evidence.

The study of past geologic events is not the normal sense of scientific study which is based on observation, experiment and repeatability. This is historical or forensic science where the past is inferred from observable evidence. As in a court of law, there may be different ways of looking at the same evidence. It is up to judge and jury to decide which interpretation makes the most sense. This book presents my interpretation of the evidence I have seen.

In the greater Portland/Vancouver area over one million people are driving through the remains of a massive disaster area and they don't even know it! Day after day they see the same landscape stretched out before them and are oblivious to the destruction wreaked upon this area. My hope is that *GigaFlood* will open your eyes to the events of the greatest of the Lake Missoula floods; showing where the floodwaters inundated, ripped-up basalt, truncated hills, carved channels and lakes, and left giant current ripples, enormous boulders, glacial erratics and scars on the land. Once you see it, you will never look at this area the same again.

Acknowledgements

A special thank you to David Alt for reviewing my first manuscript and voluntarily writing a foreword and endorsement for this book. I owe a great debt of gratitude to those who reviewed the first edition and gave me helpful suggestions.

Thank you to Scott Burns and the many others who gave their encouragement, time, insight, and knowledge from their many years of studying geology. And to the Ice Age Floods Institute and the members of the Lower Columbia Chapter who let me share my love of the subject and latest discoveries through the presentations, drive guides and many field trips I prepared. It has been fulfilling to work with the City of Tualatin and the Tualatin Historical Society which have enthusiastically promoted public awareness of the effects of the floods in their area.

Kalvin and Mike Morauske have my heartfelt appreciation for making a dream come true: to fly over and photograph flood features in eastern Washington. Also to John and Johnny Pike for flights over the Portland region. And to J.D. Mitchell for his proofreading.

Maps were created using Delorme Topo North America 9.0 except where noted. Lidar maps used courtesy of Oregon Department of Geology and Mineral Industries (DOGAMI).

All illustrations and photographs are by Rick Thompson except as indicated.

A tremendous thank you to my wife, Sylvia, for first introducing me to the Lake Missoula Flood story, joining me in my many research adventures, supporting my obsession with this book, and for her ideas and improvements to the final writing.

Introduction
The GigaFlood Story

Earth scientists are now discovering that there were many ice age floods caused by ice dams blocking rivers systems and/or catastrophic ice melting. The subject of this book is one of the first category: an ice dam blocking the Clark Fork River in northern Idaho.

While there were multiple mega-floods in eastern Washington and down the Columbia River, this book is focusing on just one – the biggest – the GigaFlood.

No one knows how many there were but it is generally agreed that the first one from Glacial Lake Missoula was the largest. A large flood occurring after several smaller floods would remove the evidence of the smaller floods. Small floods after a large one would leave traces in and on the marks left by the larger one that preceded them.

A second flood the same size as the first is highly unlikely because the first one would have enlarged the channels, including where the ice dam was, so to obtain the previous ice and water depth would require more ice and water in order to fill the areas scoured by the first.

In this book we will not speculate on how many other mega-floods there were or their size. This book is concerned only with the one that did the most to change the shape of the land it crossed. That is the GigaFlood.

The fury of nature is hard to imagine and the power of water is one of the strongest forces on earth.

Many people think of a flood as being like a river rising and flooding horizontally as it invades roads and homes, starting with a few inches and rising to several feet or more.

The GigaFlood was caused by a dam bursting – a dam built of ice. This was a massive wall of ice spurring off of the frozen continent of North America. The Canadian ice sheets (Cordilleran and Laurentide) stretched from Alaska to Greenland; from the northern most regions down across all of Canada with its fingers reaching into the northern United States. One of these fingers of ice, from the Cordilleran Ice Sheet, pushed down the Purcell Trench in northern Idaho.

As the ice advanced along the trench, it was pushed uphill over 640 feet higher by the unceasing pressure of more snow and ice building up on the ice sheet and forcing the lobe to move. A portion of it filled the mouth of the Clark Fork River at Lake Pend Oreille and acted as a cork in a bottle to stop the flow of the river. Eventually this lobe reached a height of approximately 2,500 feet above the present day lake level making a colossal dam across the river. The ice dam pushed past the mouth of the river all the way to Rathdrum Prairie just northeast of Spokane, Washington.

Later, as the climate warmed, the snow turned to rain and the ice began to melt. The previously frozen rivers and streams began to flow into the valleys and created a immense lake behind the ice dam. The lake reached a height of nearly 2,000 feet behind the dam; 1,000 feet above what is now the city of Missoula, Montana.

Suddenly the ice dam broke into millions of pieces and sent a 2,000 foot wall of water, ice and rock shooting out of the mouth of the Clark Fork like a giant fire hose. The exact cause of the failure of the ice dam is unknown; but the scars left today tell us that Glacial Lake Missoula, with 540 cubic miles of water, similar to the size of Lake Ontario and Lake Erie combined, exploded like a bomb out of its restraints and enveloped the landscape like a tsunami wave.

The water rushed out through Rathdrum Prairie into northeastern Washington dividing into hundreds of smaller, but extremely powerful, rivers and channels cutting its way across central Washington through Wallula Gap, down the Columbia River and finally to the Pacific Ocean.

As the deluge tore through the channel of the Columbia River it scoured and reshaped it into what we recognize today as the Columbia River Gorge. The river was already there but without the steep walls and the many waterfalls that we now appreciate.

This cataclysmic inundation racing across the land was not just a skyscraper size wall of water, rushing like a steam locomotive at times up to 80 miles an hour, but it carried with it the splintered bergs of ice the size of river barges and any rocks the ice had trapped during its formation. The water washed away the topsoil of eastern Washington as one would blow dust off the top of a table. It stripped the vegetation and broke any trees like matchsticks. It beat against the massive Columbia River Basalt plateau. The flowing water created vortexes which plucked sections right out of the bedrock with its powerful suction. The crashing water picked apart giant columns of basalt and tumbled these boulders like little marbles.

When all this water, rock and ice hit a constricted area they created a momentary hydraulic dam like ice bunched up at the spout of a pitcher just before it spills out. The GigaFlood backed up at Wallula Gap. It overtopped this area, ate away the sides and in pulsing fits it worked its way through. Confined in the narrow Columbia River Gorge, it rose to over 1,000 feet high and tore away the rock leaving the shear cliffs and beautiful waterfalls we admire today.

With speeds up to 60-80 mph it burst out into the Portland basin, slammed into Rocky Butte and the other hills in east Portland, gouged channels as the water came in, left huge gravel bars and cut additional channels when it departed.

The last of the hydraulic dams was at Kalama, Washington, approximately 35 miles north of Portland, Oregon. Again the water halted and backed up; this time all the way through the Willamette Valley to present day Eugene; blanketing the valley like an inland sea, to approximately 400 feet above sea level.

In northwest Oregon and southwest Washington, the roads we drive every day, the views we see around us are all a testimony to the GigaFlood – the largest of the Lake Missoula Floods. This book will reveal those features, tell you where they are and explain how they were formed. You will see this region, which you may have seen every day for many years, with new eyes and a new appreciation of the power and scope of the GigaFlood.

Chapter One
The Ice Age
("Last Glacial Maximum")

To understand the GigaFlood we must first understand the ice age, how it formed and how it created these floods.

What scientists call "the last ice age" or "the last glacial maximum" was so large that it covered all or most areas thought to have been affected by earlier ice ages. For that reason this book will refer only to that last ice age. It is the only one for which we have unequivocal direct evidence and is the only one that bears on the subject of this book.

There are as many as 40 or more theories of why the earth experienced an ice age. The one that is most popular right now is the "Astronomical Theory of Climate Change" or Milankovitch theory proposed by Serbian geophysicist and astronomer Milutin Milanković (May 28, 1879 – December 12, 1958), and published in multiple books and papers between 1912 and 1944. It uses math to show that if the earth were to travel on an irregular ellipse around and away from the sun every 100,000 years or so it could cause global cooling.

But that's not an ice age. An ice age is defined as a time when there is a massive build-up of ice and snow near the poles. And to get that build-up there needs to be a high rate of precipitation. The atmosphere's ability to hold moisture increases with heat and drops as the temperature cools. You may have heard the term: "It's too cold to snow." If it were much colder in the winters it would be like Siberia where it gets very cold but does not snow much at all. If the earth were too cold, the atmosphere would not carry the moisture needed to fall as snow and accumulate as the great ice sheets. This is why a cooling of the whole earth could never produce an ice age.

What is needed is lots of ocean evaporation to fall as rain and snow on the continents. For this a heat source is required in order to evaporate immense amounts of ocean water. What could heat the oceans? Underwater volcanism and earthquakes could.

But evaporation alone isn't enough either because the clouds have to be forced to relinquish their moisture in the form of rain and snow.

In the tropics, above a rain forest, the atmosphere may become super-saturated to the point that it can't hold any more liquid and the water vapor will condense into rain. But away from the tropics, all precipitation starts out as what is known as cloud condensation nuclei (CCN) forming around microscopic dust. Meteorologists call this the: Bergeron or "cold-rain" process.

To get a large amount of rain and snow we need a large amount of atmospheric dust. Without the dust, the ice particles will never condense and form snow or rain. For an ice age, you need prodigious amounts of snow and rain and for that you would need prodigious amounts of dust in the upper atmosphere. This dust has to be continually re-supplied for the entire time of the ice build-up.

Next, you need slightly cooler summers that do not allow the snow to melt. As each winter's snow accumulates year after year and with little or no summer-time melting, you get an ice build-up that can lead to an ice age.

It is estimated that the ice sheets were two miles or more thick during the ice age holding so much of the earth's water supply that the sea level world-wide was between 200 and 400 feet lower than it is now. That is a lot of ice!

What could have caused these three things to happen: ocean evaporation, dust in the upper atmosphere, and cooler summer temperatures? Volcanoes and super-volcanoes. Volcanism and tectonic action in the oceans would heat up the water allowing the evaporation. We know that an El Niño, a small warming of the Pacific Ocean, affects world climate. Think of a massive El Niño, or thousands of El Niños. There are over 2,000 known volcanoes in the Pacific Ocean alone.

Land volcanoes, like the 30 mile wide Yellowstone caldera, considered an ice age volcano, belched billions of tons of volcanic ash into the atmosphere. This ash could have provided the dust for the cloud condensing nuclei needed for snow and brought about a cooler climate by reflecting the sun's heat back out into space.

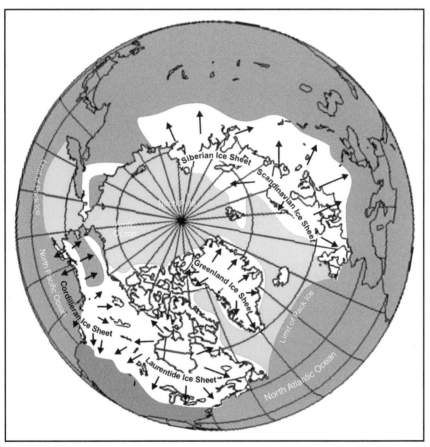

Northern Hemisphere during the ice age
(Note that the north pole is not in the center of the ice)

The year 1816 was called "the year without a summer" partly because in 1815 there were a number of major volcanic eruptions capped by the eruption of Mount Tambora in Indonesia; the largest known eruption in over 1,300 years.

Most people have the idea that the ice was centered right over the poles. This was not the case. The ice sheets formed first over the continents where the wind currents, carrying the water vapor from the warm oceans, crossed land masses where it was cold. For much of the time that ice was building up on the continents the polar oceans remained free of ice due to warm water.

Towards the end of the Ice Age the oceans themselves cooled. But the atmosphere still contained enough dust to block the sun's heat and this allowed the polar oceans in the midst of the ice to freeze into what is called pack ice. Some of this pack ice is still with us today, telling us that we are not totally out of the ice age.

Chapter Two
Ice Sheets and Ice Lobes

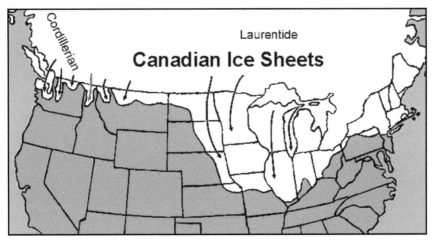

The Canadian Ice Sheets spawned dozens of ice lobes (some indicated by arrows) including the Purcell Lobe (red arrow) that dammed the Clark Fork River in northern Idaho

As glacial snow, snow that lands on an ice sheet, ice lobe, or a glacier, builds up it undergoes several changes. It gets tightly packed together into glacial ice. This differs from ice formed by freezing water because it traps both dust and air in the ice. Eventually these tiny air pockets become compressed. In fact, glacial ice put in a glass of water fizzes as the air bubbles are released.

Once the ice is about 60 feet thick, the pressure from the weight above causes the crystals to rearrange themselves. Instead of pointing every which way as in the snow, the ice crystals flatten out and align themselves horizontally. This allows the ice to slide on itself and makes movement possible.

Mountain glaciers (also known as alpine glaciers) form by the accumulation of snow in the mountains. Once they are thick enough they can begin their process of creeping down the slope. Several things cause a glacier to move: 1) the amount of ice, 2) the gradient of the slope, and 3) the temperature. If it is warm enough for the ice to start melting then the water will trickle its way to the bottom and act as a lubricant allowing the glacier to move. Usually glaciers move at a glacial pace (pun intended) but some glaciers seldom move. Palmer Glacier on Mount Hood, according to Portland State University, is actually a stationary snowfield. Some glaciers have been known to gallop at incredible speeds if conditions are right. When a glacier does move, it follows the terrain downward, being pulled by gravity.

As a glacier rides over the terrain along its path it scratches and gouges and plucks up rocks that act as chisels and do more scratching and gouging. It then carries the rocks and rock dust, called rock flour, with it.

Simplified illustration of a mountain glacier

If the glacier ends on land it will often leave a pile of rocks known as a "terminal moraine."

If the glacier ends in a body of water, it will calve off floating icebergs. Some of these may contain rocks that were incorporated into the glacier and they will travel as "iceberg erratics" (ice-rafted boulders) to wherever the iceberg takes them.

Mountain/alpine glaciers flow from a higher to lower elevation whereas ice sheets radiate out from a higher center created by a thicker accumulation of snow and ice.

An ice sheet (also called a continental glacier) is hundreds or thousands of miles wide and is thickest at the center of the sheet where the most snow has fallen. The increased weight from the accumulation of snow and ice at the center tends to push outward making the ice sheet wider. It is like someone making bread or playing with clay where they push down in the middle and the dough or clay moves out from the center toward the sides. Eventually fingers of ice will push off from the ice sheet forming ice lobes.

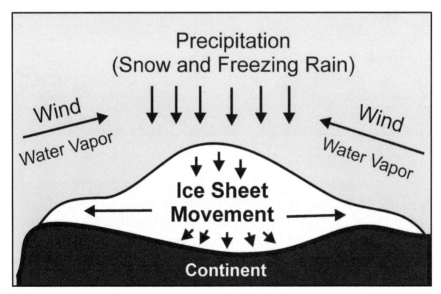

Simplified illustration of an ice sheet

Ice sheets contain so much water that the weight actually pushes down the land on which it sits. The earth is plastic enough that it can sink as weight is added and then rebound as the ice is removed. Geologists call this "isostatic equilibrium."

Ice sheets move extremely slowly except at the edges where it forms ice lobes. Ice lobes move because of the pressure of the ice from the dense center of the ice sheet that is pushing them. Because of this weight the ice lobes are forced to move, even uphill, away from the center.

In an ice lobe, as well as in a mountain glacier, the top and middle moves faster than the parts in contact with the land. This has been demonstrated by pounding stakes into glaciers and coming back later and seeing that the stakes in the center have moved much farther than those near the edges.

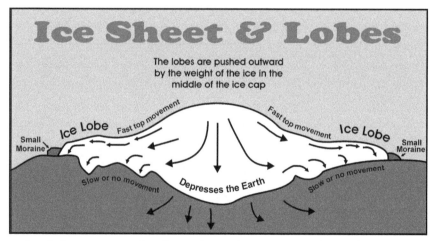

Ice lobes are pushed out from the center of the ice sheet

An ice lobe that is pushed over a rise and then downhill will act as an alpine glacier, scraping and sliding downhill. But the Purcell Lobe, the ice lobe that impounded Glacial Lake Missoula, rose in elevation from north to south along the Purcell Trench.

The speed and distance that an ice lobe moves is determined by the height of the ice sheet. As long as the ice is growing deeper on the ice sheet, the lobe will keep moving, but as soon as the ice sheet discontinues its growth, the lobe will stop growing. Remember this is not a mountain/alpine glacier and is not being pulled down hill by gravity.

The alpine glaciers on the sides of the Purcell Trench joined the ice lobe which filled the valley below. In doing so the alpine glaciers contributed their load of rocks that they had picked up coming down the side valleys to those picked up by the lobe itself.

These are the rocks that then became erratic boulders when the ice lobe broke into icebergs that were carried hundreds of miles on the Lake Missoula flood waters.

With the top and center moving faster than the bottom and sides, a glacier acts as a conveyor belt bringing rocks forward and dumping them at the end to form a moraine. This happens even when it has not acted as a road grader pushing rocks in front of it. There are times when weather and snowfall allowed the ice to melt back or advance forward leaving multiple moraines. It is sometimes difficult to determine if this is evidence of multiple glaciations or just advances and retreats of the same ice. The evidence tends to look very much the same.

A "snow-line" (also called: an Equilibrium Line) is an imaginary line across a continent, and on the sides of mountains, at which point the precipitation changes from snow to rain. North of this line on a continent and up from the line on a mountain, the precipitation is snow or freezing rain. South and below this line it falls just as rain. This snow-line moves with the weather; south and down when it is colder, north and up when it is warmer.

The Purcell Ice Lobe formed at the height of the ice age when the ice was accumulating in the center of the Cordilleran Ice Sheet and pushing out at the edges. Then the snow-line was south of the Clark Fork River. As a result very little liquid water was going into the streams that would normally feed the main river drainage. It was all falling as snow and adding to the mountain glaciers that filled the valleys of the northern Rocky Mountains.

Toward the end of the ice age the temperatures rose and the falling snow turned to rain. The Purcell Ice Lobe stopped growing and even started to melt. The mountain glaciers started to melt and flow down into the Clark Fork River. But the ice lobe, blocking the river outlet, was over 2,000 feet high, 20 to 30 miles across, and many miles long. The water had nowhere to go except to fill up the valleys behind the ice dam and form Glacial Lake Missoula.

During the summers, some of the ice would melt and the lake would grow, but as the colder months arrived, the water flowing into the lake would slow or even stop, being frozen in glaciers and snow packs until the next thaw.

During the winters, while the lake level sat at the same elevation, wave action and wind-blown floating ice could chisel away at the shoreline of the lake. This could be what formed the strand lines that now delineate the shores of the lake. These are not like the lines in the mud at the bottom of a reservoir that has been drawn down. These are cut into the rock of the hillside and have not eroded away since the last lake filling.

These horizontal lines are visible today on Mount Sentinel and Mount Jumbo, east and north of Missoula and elsewhere around the valleys of northwest Montana. They are best seen at dawn or dusk and when there is a light dusting of snow.

Lake Missoula strandlines on hillside in the Bitterroot Valley south of Missoula, Montana

No one has been able to accurately count the strandlines that formed as bathtub rings around Glacial Lake Missoula. This is because the water never stood at one level for a very long period of time. But the subtle lines seem to be roughly 20 feet apart indicating an annual rise of about 20 feet of snow melt in the lake.

Strandlines on Mt. Jumbo

Some have suggested that each line could represent a separate lake filling and draining, but it is improbable that a new lake filling would consistently be approximately 20 feet above (or below) the previous filling. And the lines could not have formed as the lake level fell after the collapse of the ice dam because it is thought that the lake emptied in two to three days, not leaving time to sit at one level long enough to cut a line into the hillside.

The highest of these strandlines are almost 900 feet above present day Missoula, Montana at 4,200 feet above today's sea level. Scour lines at the mouth of the Clark Fork River confirm that this was the deepest lake level. This put the water at nearly 2,000 feet deep at the ice dam.

At this point something had to give. Ice does not stand the test as a permanent dam.

There are three main theories about why the dam broke: 1) the water over-topped the dam and eroded it away from the top down, 2) water undercut or lifted the ice dam from below causing it to fail catastrophically, 3) water seeped through tiny holes in the dam using capillary action at first and then tunneling through the dam until it failed.

A fourth possibility for what caused the ice dam to collapse catastrophically is that an earthquake, or even multiple earthquakes fractured the dam. The earthquakes could easily have been triggered by the 56.7 million tons of the water behind the dam.

Water related earthquakes were first documented during the filling of Lake Mead behind Hoover Dam in the 1940s. The quakes continued as the reservoir deepened until it reached the top and stabilized. Since that time over 100 hydroelectric dams world-wide have recorded earthquakes. And these dams have much less than a 2,000 foot deep lake pressing against them.

Geologists now believe that the filling of the Zipingpu dam on the Min River near the city of Dujiangyan, Sichuan Province in southwest China could have led to the massive 7.9 magnitude earthquake on May 12, 2008 killing 80,000 people.

Whatever caused it, the dam broke and the entire contents of Glacial Lake Missoula emptied in as little as two days. This was the GigaFlood!

The 9-Mile Formation, west of Missoula, exposes sediments from the bottom of Glacial Lake Missoula. The dark and light alternating layers (once thought to represent separate lake fillings) are now thought by some to represent seasonal deposits while the lake filled.

Chapter Three
The Lake Missoula Floods

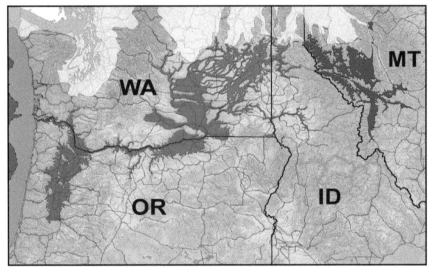

Areas affected by the Lake Missoula Floods
(Figure prepared by Jones and Jones)

There are two types of floods: meteorological and outburst but their effects are totally different.

A meteorological flood is caused by weather: rain and melting snow and ice and is fed by many streams and rivulets as it flows downstream. Continuous or heavy rains will saturate the ground and so the water is not absorbed into it. Because of this and the repeated addition of more water, the flood increases in volume the farther it moves from its starting point. It generally reaches its maximum size and strength at or near where it flows into a larger stream or body of water.

An outburst flood, as its name implies, is caused by a blockage of some sort that is then removed allowing the water to burst out.

It might be a man-made dam that fails, a rock slide that temporarily blocks a stream or a glacier that blocks a stream or river. An outburst flood only has one source (although the river may have many) and that is where the blockage is. This type of flood is the largest and most powerful at the point of the outburst. As it flows downstream, it has friction against the sides and bottom of the channel, obstacles it must confront, and wide flat areas where it spreads out and slows down. It also tends to leave portions of itself in pools and saturated soils in areas outside the main channel. This means that unlike a meteorological flood, an outburst flood gets smaller and weaker the farther it gets from the outburst.

The Lake Missoula Floods were outburst floods and therefore were the biggest and most violent where the dam broke. Then as they spread out to cover a 3,000 square mile area of central Washington, they slowed and lost both water and energy. This pattern of spreading out was repeated multiple times as the floods worked their way downstream. It has been said by at least one geologist that there were probably only about five that were big enough by the time they made it through the Columbia River Gorge to have any major affect on the Willamette Valley. This is part of the on-going research to unravel the many mysteries of the floods story.

The GigaFlood got its start when the Purcell Ice Lobe filled the area that is now Lake Pend Oreille (pond oh ray) at the mouth of the Clark Fork River, in Idaho. This river was originally called "Clarks Fork of the Columbia," named for William Clark. A lobe of the western Canadian ice sheet, also called the Cordilleran Ice Sheet, moved south through the Purcell Trench into what is now the Idaho panhandle between the Selkirk and the Cabinet Mountains to at least the south end of Lake Pend Oreille.

Where the ice lobe crossed the Canadian border the elevation is 1,756 feet. Where it entered what is now Lake Pend Oreille the elevation is 2,070 feet. At the south end of the lake the shore over which the ice lobe moved is over 2,400 feet high. The base of the ice moved 640 feet higher in a little over 80 miles. This has led to some debate on how fast the ice dam could rebuild itself. I have heard people say it took as little as 12 years to rebuild or as much as 40 or 50 years or even 100 years between floods.

Because the ice lobe moved "down" the Purcell Trench it is easy to think of it moving down in elevation like a mountain glacier. Instead, it was actually moving up hill.

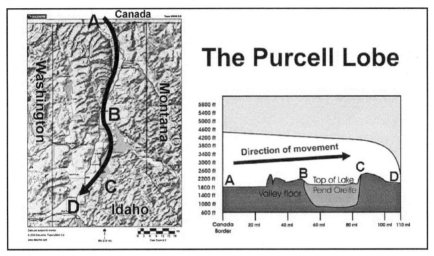

Diagram showing the location of the Purcell lobe in northern Idaho and its upward movement from 1,756 to 2,400 feet

In crossing the Clark Fork River it effectively dammed the entire river drainage for all of northwest Montana and created a lake as the water backed up into the valleys of the Rocky Mountains as far as 250 miles. This included not only the Clark Fork River but also the Bitterroot and Flathead Rivers and all of their tributaries.

Estimates for the thickness of the ice dam are between 2,500 to 5,000 feet thick. The height of the water behind the ice dam was about 2,000 feet deep. This wall of ice held back 540 cubic miles of water. The pressure on the ice lobe was tremendous.

The lake filled the entire Clark Fork basin between the Bitterroot Mountains and the Swan Range. It eventually covered 3,000 square miles of northwest Montana with about the same volume of water as Lake Erie and Lake Ontario combined.

At the same time that the Purcell Lobe was creating a blockage on the Clark Fork River, the Okanogan Lobe was blocking the Columbia River near today's site of Grand Coulee Dam. This created Glacial Lake Columbia and diverted the Columbia River, first through Moses Coulee and then Grand Coulee. Grand Coulee is 50 miles long, up to 6 miles wide and nearly 1,000 feet deep in places. This was the largest of the Lake Missoula flood channels.

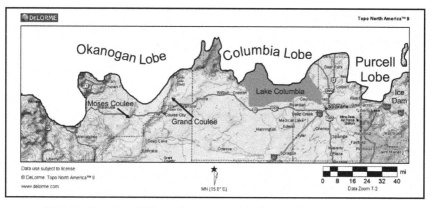

North Central Washington with ice lobes, coulees
and Glacial Lake Columbia

Looking out the mouth of the Clark Fork River where the
entire contents of Glacial Lake Missoula emptied in just two
to three days

Lake Pend Oreille, the site of the ice dam, viewed from near the mouth of the Clark Fork River

Eventually the ice dam failed. When it broke it sent an initial 2,000 foot wall of water racing across eastern Washington, spreading out, joining with Glacial Lake Columbia and eroding both the soil and even the basalt bedrock everywhere it could find or create a channel. It filled ravines, then spilled over and filled more ravines. It crossed and re-crossed its own path which formed a braided bed roughly 100 miles wide and covered 3,000 square miles of the Columbia Plateau. In the process it removed an astonishing 50 cubic miles of rock and soil from what became the Channeled Scablands in eastern Washington.

The GigaFlood rushed across the landscape and converged at Wallula Gap where the Columbia River cuts through the Horse Heaven Hills of eastern Washington. Much like filling the bathtub faster than it can run out the drain, the water rose to over 1,000 feet behind the narrow outlet forming what some geologists call a hydraulic dam.

Wallula Gap from the south - Jim Willison photo

Approximately 200 cubic miles of water per day was rushing toward Wallula Gap but; even today, it is only wide enough for 40 cubic miles per day to go through. Wallula Gap was widened by the abrasive action of the water, ice and rock that was being forced through it. In the mean-time it formed a large temporary lake we call Lake Lewis.

The water shot through the gap much like water under pressure jetting out of a fire hose. It removed several thick layers of basalt lava leaving erosional remnants like Hat Rock and Twin Sisters to remind us of what had been there before. These are tiny remnants of lava flows that stretched for many miles.

Hat Rock (named by Lewis and Clark) is another erosional remnant near the out flow of Wallula Gap

Twin Sisters, erosional remnants in Wallula Gap

Down river from the gap the water spread out again depositing the sand and gravel that makes up the rich farm soil around Hermiston, Oregon. Here it formed a large temporary lake we call Lake Condon, named for Thomas Condon, first professor of geology at the University of Oregon and Oregon's first State Geologist.

From there the waters converged in the channel of the pre-existing Columbia River which was the only path available where it could cut through the Cascade Range.

Chapter Four
Discovering the Floods

The geography of eastern Washington that first intrigued J Harlen Bretz in the early 20th century was like nothing else he had ever seen. His interest was piqued when he saw a topographic map of Potholes Cataract. This showed a strange-looking double horseshoe cliff with small lakes at the bottom and another cliff away from the horseshoes where the whole thing seemed to drop off into the Columbia River. Above the horseshoes were more small lakes and long vertical grooves pointing toward the two cliffs.

Geologist J Harlen Bretz
(1882 - 1981)
Photo from plaque at Dry Falls

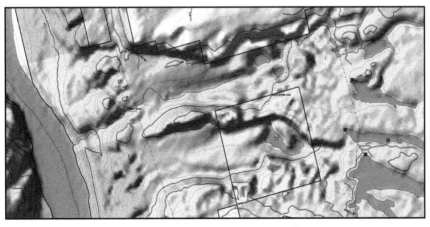

Topographic map of Potholes Cataract

Bretz was teaching at Franklin High School and then at the University of Washington in Seattle, an area formed totally by glaciers. The area east of the Cascade Mountain range was supposed to have also been formed by glaciers during the ice age, but he knew of no glacial terrain like what he was seeing in the map of Potholes Cataract. And he knew of no glacial action that could create such an odd landform.

In 1922, he started spending his summers investigating the other-worldly landscapes east of the mountains. What he found were long deep canyons with straight sides and flat bottoms, teardrop shaped hills on high ground, 300-foot high mounds of rocks in the bends of the channels and more horseshoe-shaped cliffs within the channels.

Glaciers don't make those sorts of features. Water does, but this would require an amazing amount of water, far more than had ever been seen on the land anywhere except in stationary lakes. But this water had to have been moving at tremendous speeds.

He surmised that there had been a huge flood that swept into Washington near where the City of Spokane is now. It swept across eastern Washington and into the Columbia River where it coursed downstream to the Pacific Ocean. Nothing but a huge "Spokane Flood" could have shaped the land into what he called the "Channeled Scablands." The farmers and ranchers had already named the rocky, barren patches as scabland, but Bretz noticed that these formations were in parallel lines, eventually flowing toward Wallula Gap, where the Columbia cuts through a row of hills. So he called them the "Channeled Scablands."

Bretz also knew that glaciers leave behind lateral moraines along the sides of its path and terminal moraines where they stop. There are no moraines in the channeled scablands except one at the head of Moses Coulee that was set in place by the Okanogan Ice Lobe after the coulee was cut.

There was nothing "normal" about whatever it was that created the channeled scablands. Now we know that there are other places like these, even on Mars. But, at the time, no one besides Bretz seemed to understand that they were created by massive amounts of fast moving water.

When he wrote of his discoveries and offered them up to the Geological Society of America in 1923, it was as if he had offended the sensibilities of all the older, more well-known geologists through an unforgivable faux pas. A huge flood was not part of geology at the time! It ran against the tide of the principle of "uniformitarianism" which geologists had pushed hard to implement since the late 1700's.

In simple terms uniformitarianism says that all the land forms visible today were formed by the processes we see today. This was really an idea that could not be scientifically tested and thus un-provable (not falsifiable), but it was the template in use at the time. There was no room for catastrophes of any sort and especially a watery one. It seemed too Biblical which was one of the things uniformitarianism was established to avoid.

Bretz was laughed at, ridiculed and scorned for his "outrageous hypotheses" for 40 years. Eventually, many of his critics had retired or died and a new group of geologists were willing to look at the evidence. They did this in the summer of 1967 and came to the startling conclusion that Bretz was right. Nothing but a flood of huge proportions could have shaped the land in eastern Washington. The strongest evidence seems to have been Dry Falls, one of the double horseshoe cliffs with the lakes below in the center of a 50-mile long channel. It had to have been formed by fast moving water – a waterfall far larger than any on earth, that was now a dry and mute testimony to its once awesome power.

Geology can point to that day as the death knell of uniformitarianism and the birth of "neo-catastrophism" which is the present prevailing paradigm. It says that catastrophes can and do shape the earth in ways not seen today. Plate tectonics, super-volcanism and meteorite strikes have come along as theories to bolster the neo-catastrophic way of thinking.

Water can be an immensely powerful force. I know of two times in history when high-pressure water has been used to wash down hillsides. Once was in the California gold rush when miners used water from high pressure monitors to wash entire hillsides through their sluice boxes to recover the gold. They washed so much dirt into the rivers that the California government outlawed the practice in 1884 because it was clogging streams as well as flooding and destroying farmland in the Sacramento delta.

The other time was when the City of Seattle, Washington washed whole hills into Puget Sound to make level land for their city. Called the "Denny Re-grade" the operation went on between 1897 and 1911.

From this we know that water is a very strong erosive agent, especially when it is moving very fast. That is what we had in eastern Washington when the Purcell Ice Lobe broke and released a 2,000 foot high wall of water moving between 50 and 80 mph. There is not much that could have stood in its way.

First of all it scoured out Lake Pend Oreille where the ice dam had been. The lake is still over 1,000 feet deep, even after thousands of years of glacial melting and silting in.

The high speed water hit the hills of eastern Washington with its covering of 100 to 300 feet of soft Palouse loess soil and didn't slow down but immediately started attacking the basalt bed rock.

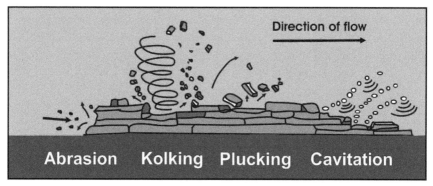

The four main types of erosion in a fast moving flood

There are four distinct ways that high-volume, fast-moving water can quickly erode even the hardest rock: abrasion, kolking, plucking and cavitation.

Abrasion is where the sheer force of the water combined with rock and sand scour the upstream and top surfaces of the rock.

Kolking is an underwater vortex that acts as a tornado, picking up bedrock and tossing it aside just as a normal tornado can throw around houses and cars. When the flood is gone it leaves holes in the bedrock (called kolk depressions, kolk ponds or kolk lakes) as well as huge boulders somewhere downstream.

Plucking, as its name implies is where rock is simply plucked up by the force of the water and carried away.

Cavitation is caused by fast moving water creating tiny vacuum bubbles as it moves over a rough surface. Due to the force and speed of the water a vacuum bubble will stretch and enlarge, but it is still just a vacuum, a hole with nothing in it! Eventually it collapses with extreme force. The implosion of these tiny vacuum bubbles is so powerful that this acts as tiny jackhammers beating against the rock and actually pulverizing it.

Cavitation was demonstrated in 1983 when fast moving water ate a huge hole in one of the spillway tunnels at Glen Canyon Dam in Arizona. It cut through the three foot thick steel reinforced concrete and made a 32 foot deep, 40 foot wide and 150 foot long hole in the tunnel's concrete flooring in mere minutes. It took 63,000 cubic feet of concrete to fill the hole and repair the 40 foot diameter spillway tunnel.

The ice age floods used all these techniques to strip off roughly 50 cubic miles of rock and soil from eastern Washington.

There isn't much that can stand up to high pressure water, but after all rock is rock and is both hard and heavy. Basalt rock though has a weakness. When basalt cools, it shrinks. It can not shrink as a total mass of hundreds of square miles. So it shrinks in smaller bits and forms cracks between each piece of rock.

Basalt cools and shrinks into two main patterns. Fast surface cooling seems to form many inter-locking odd-shaped blocks. In the basalt flow, this forms the top section, called the entablature and is described as having a hacky or brick-a-brack appearance.

The lower part of the flow, which is insulated by the upper part, cools more slowly and forms five or six-sided columns; called the colonnade. These columns vary in size from a few inches across to several yards and from 1 foot to 30 or more feet long. Most are less than a foot across and less than 10 feet long.

Pillow lava under basalt columns near The Dalles, Oregon

A general pattern for a basalt flow is vertical columns on the bottom and the brick-a-brack style entablature on top. But this is not always what we see. Sometimes we only see the entablature part or the colonnade part and not both. Sometimes the top is very thick with short columns below. Or it might be the opposite. Gas bubbles within the lava will form a frothy layer called "vesicular" lava at the top.

When the base of a flow encounters water it often forms pillow lava and an orange mineral called palagonite. Pillow lava forms under water as the surface of the lava cools forming a rounded blob; but the inside is still flowing, so it bursts out and forms another blob. These "pillows" can stack up into very thick sections of the flow. This process has been filmed in Hawaii where the lava flows into the ocean.

Basalt flows exposed in Wallula Gap with talus slopes below
- Pike Pictures photo

Most interesting is when the columns form horizontally or in a radial pattern or curved and bent in the middle. The various patterns add to the mystique of the Columbia River Basalt Plateau.

But the point of this is that basalt is filled with cracks that make it easy to erode. Given time a basalt cliff will crumble into pieces that fall down creating what is called a talus slope.

One of the main ways this happens is in the winter when rain water seeps into the cracks in the basalt and then freezes. The freezing expands the water into ice which forces the crack a tiny bit wider. Eventually it will widen the crack to the point that the rock falls away from the cliff and becomes part of the talus slope.

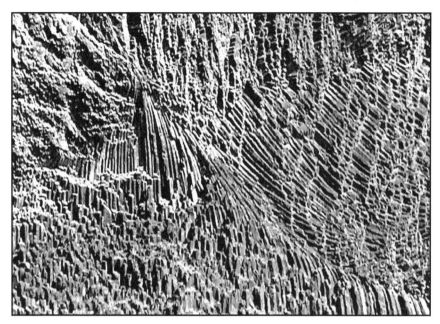

A complex cooling pattern in the basalt wall of Grand Coulee in central Washington - Mark Martin photo

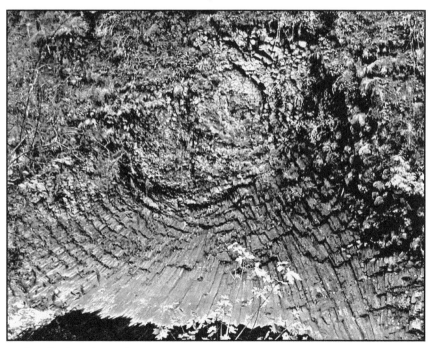

Radiating basalt columns on the Molalla River in Oregon

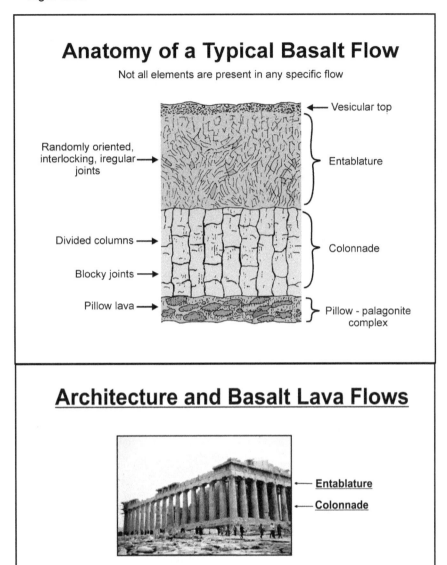

Anatomy of a Typical Basalt Flow

Not all elements are present in any specific flow

- Vesicular top
- Randomly oriented, interlocking, iregular joints
- Entablature
- Divided columns
- Colonnade
- Blocky joints
- Pillow lava
- Pillow - palagonite complex

Architecture and Basalt Lava Flows

- Entablature
- Colonnade

- Cornice
- Frieze
- Architrave
- Entablature
- Capital
- Column

Where columnar basalt gets its descriptive names

Lower Palouse Canyon in southeastern Washington

Scoured basalt bedrock. Note the trim line in the top of the
photo (arrow). That was the height of the flood waters,
leaving the Palouse silt above that elevation undisturbed.
- Pike Pictures photo

At the end of the GigaFlood there was no talus because the fast-moving water had carried all the loose rocks away from the cliffs depositing them in wide boulder fields or gravel bars as much as 400 feet high and miles long.

In places like the outlet of Grand Coulee and below Sentinel Gap the boulder fields are miles across and filled with millions of rocks.

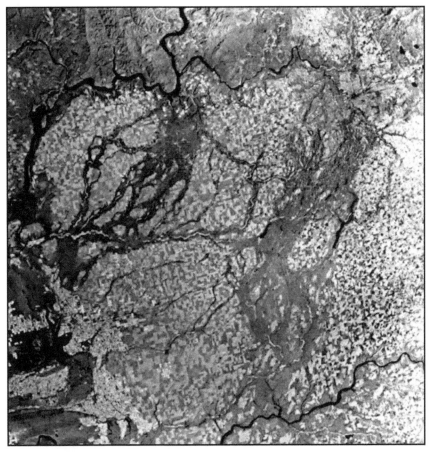

Satellite photo of eastern Washington's Channeled Scablands - NASA photo

Chapter Five
The Channeled Scablands

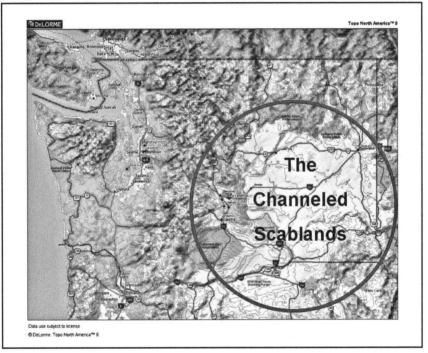

Map of Washington State showing the location of the
Channeled Scablands

Covering about three quarters of eastern Washington, the
Channeled Scablands are a strange land of soft rolling silt hills
dissected by sharp, steep-sided canyons, dry waterfalls, ponds,
gravel mountains and huge fields of rocks, from small stones to
giant boulders. It is no wonder the farmers called the dry bare
channels "scablands" because of their scab-like looks and near
uselessness for farming.

Today the Channeled Scablands of eastern Washington are visible from space because the bare bedrock differs so much from the rest of the land. In the years since the last of these floods very little soil has filled in the flood channels.

The Channeled Scablands etch the Columbia Plateau somewhat like motor bike trails scar a barren hillside near a big city. The trails all run in roughly the same direction, but tend to blend and cross each other, separating and merging in irregular patterns before reaching their destination.

A motor bike rider's objective might be to reach the highest point while on the Columbia Plateau the water's destination was the lowest elevation.

The Columbia Plateau is also referred to as the Columbia Basin, because it is ringed with mountains. This 100,000 square mile area is bounded on the north by the Okanogan Highlands, on the east by the Rockies, on the south by the Blue Mountains and on the west by the Cascades. The whole area is tipped from the northeast toward the south with a drop of about 2,300 feet.

Moses Coulee, an excellent example of a scabland flood channel with straight sides and a flat bottom

This slope is criss-crossed with mostly dry canyons called coulees. "Coulee" comes from a French word roughly translated "to flow," but refers more to a box shaped flood channel. These were cut by the ice age floods and then left high and dry as we see them today. They have vertical sides and flat bottoms.

The entire area is underlain by a volcanic rock known as basalt which flowed out of long fissures (called "feeder dikes") from magma chambers near the Oregon-Idaho border. As a thick liquid it flowed quickly to fill in low areas and then to blanket the whole region. Many flows, one atop another, filled the Columbia Plateau with as much as 15,000 feet or more before the lava stopped flowing. Much of this lava field is below sea level so we usually only see a small portion; the upper top layers above the ground.

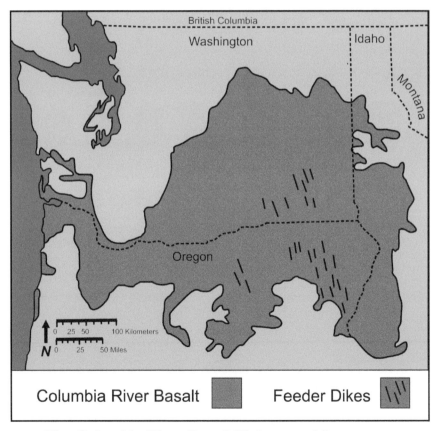

The Columbia River Basalt Plateau and its sources

Basalt is very hard rock, but easily eroded under high velocity water. The irregular and columnar joining made for easy removal of large amounts of the rock during the ice age floods.

Until the daring and stubborn geologist, J Harlen Bretz, with insight beyond most of his peers, walked these scablands it was generally assumed that they were the product of normal erosion or perhaps were cut by glaciers during the ice age or by glacial meltwater at the end of the ice age. Bretz knew different. He knew that rivers cut V-shaped valleys and glaciers cut U-shaped valleys. The coulees of eastern Washington; however, were steep-sided, flat-bottomed trenches looking as if the square blade of a huge earth-moving machine had recently gouged them.

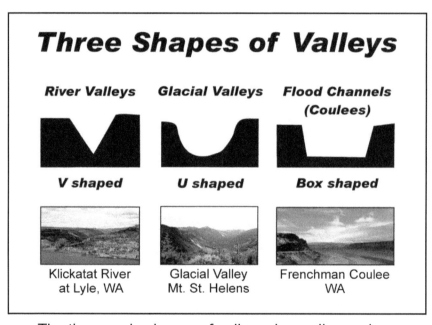

The three main shapes of valleys depending on how they were formed

A fourth valley shape which is very common (especially in the scablands) is the "incised valley," with an underfit stream in the bottom. This is where a valley was cut by something much larger than the present-day stream. Given enough time, the stream will cut down and the sides will erode to form a V-shaped valley.

Fourth Valley Shape

Underfit Stream Valleys

Incised Valley

Upper Palouse Canyon

Lower Palouse Canyon

Underfit stream or incised valley

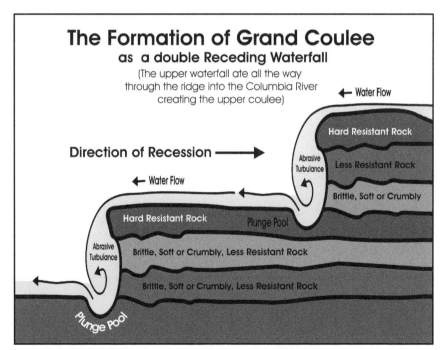

Grand Coulee was formed by two receding waterfalls, the upper one about 30 miles upstream of the lower one

The largest of the flood channels is Grand Coulee. It is approximately 50 miles long, 6 miles wide and nearly 1,000 feet deep. It is separated into upper and lower Grand Coulee by Dry Falls which is 3.5 miles wide with a drop of 400 feet. By comparison, Niagara Falls is 1 mile wide and drops 165 feet.

Dry Falls was formed by what geologists call "headward erosion." It started about 16 miles south of Dry Falls near present day Soap Lake. The falls retreated to where it is in the same way that Niagara Gorge was formed below Niagara Falls.

This is called a "receding waterfall." The water tumbled over the falls and undercut the lip of the falls until it collapsed and receded upstream. Grand Coulee actually was created by two receding waterfalls one almost 30 miles ahead of the other.

Steamboat Rock stands over 700 feet above the man-made Banks Lake that now fills the Upper Grand Coulee

Dry Falls with Umatilla Rock in the center - Pike Pictures photo

"The Feathers" an erosional remnant in Frenchman Coulee

A rock climber makes his way up one of the "Feathers"

Agatha Tower: another erosional remnant in Frenchman
Coulee

Palouse soil, tear-drop shaped, streamlined hills sculpted by the water flowing around them. These are near the Snake River in southeastern Washington.

The first waterfall receded all the way to the Columbia River in the area of Grand Coulee Dam and ate through all the layers of rock. All that is left of the upper waterfall is Steamboat Rock, a remnant in the middle of a double cataract (like Frenchman Coulee or Lower Grand Coulee) that the falls left stranded when it cut through into the Columbia River. Umatilla Rock at Dry Falls is the same kind of erosional remnant.

Over laying the basalt, in eastern Washington, is a thick strata of soil called the "Palouse Silt" or "loess." It is up to 200 feet deep in areas and completely absent in areas that were swept clean by the ice age floods. This soil is extremely stable and will hold perpendicular hill sides and road cuts. This made for teardrop shaped islands of soil (easily seen from the air) in the midst of flood scoured channels.

Remember, the floods carved away approximately 50 cubic miles of earth and then redistributed it downstream as boulder-strewn fields and massive gravel bars and broad soil plains.

Boulder field near Ephrata, Washington - Pike Pictures photo

One of several house-sized boulders plucked out of bedrock
and then dropped down stream

Huge 300 foot high gravel bar in Moses Coulee

Boulder field near Wanapum Dam south of Sentinel Gap

The end of a half-mile row of boulders along Highway 243

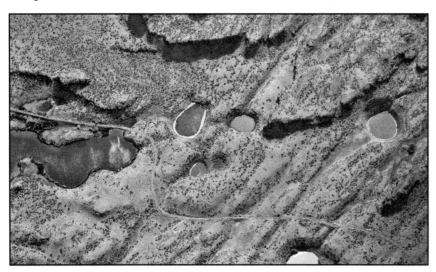

Longitudinal grooves and potholes across the basalt bedrock
produced by the Lake Missoula Floods - Pike Pictures photo

Some of the bars were shaped by the inundating water into
giant current ripples as high as 65 feet tall. Some of the boulders
that it tossed around like pebbles were as large as houses and
weighed as much as 200 tons. Much of the soil eventually made it
to the Pacific Ocean at the mouth of the Columbia, where it left
shifting bars that are navigational hazards to this day.

West Bar, 22 miles south of Wenatchee, nearly 6 miles long,
3 miles wide, and almost 200 feet high

Mid Canyon Bar, where Highway 261 crosses the Snake River, is 2.5 miles long, 0.5 miles wide and 180 feet high

The GigaFlood left a trim line on the truncated hills in the background. Highway 12 cuts through the undulating loess from lower left corner to center right.

The channeled scablands are full of amazing evidences of these tremendous floods. Besides the coulees and their erosional remnants there are huge boulder fields with millions of rocks.

There are potholes big enough to hold houses, long grooves in the bedrock, and massive gravel bars with giant current ripples. There also are the enigmatic "mima mounds" by the millions.

After the GigaFlood a soft layer of volcanic ash was deposited over much of the landscape. In some places that ash, and in other places soft silt, was somehow gathered up into rounded hills called "mima mounds." They were first named after a field of them south of Tacoma, Washington called "Mima Prairie."

At first they were thought to be Indian burial mounds and were given the Indian name: meme or mima - which means "dead." When investigated it was found that there were no human remains or even artifacts in them, so burial mounds they were not.

But the name stuck, at least in the Pacific Northwest. Other names are "pimple mounds," "natural mounds," or "prairie mounds."

Mima mounds surround a ranch in central Washington

There have been many other theories of how mima mounds came to be. It has been suggested that they are the left-over effects of permafrost during the ice age, but they are found in areas that were not affected by permafrost.

Mima mounds on top of ripples on top of a gravel bar

The main theory, the "Fossorial Rodent Hypothesis," is that they were created by giant gophers during the ice age when some animals attained great size, or perhaps even modern pocket gophers. But gophers like to tunnel deep enough to avoid winter cold and most mima mounds are on hard basalt or hard-packed gravel beds with no way to tunnel below the mound itself.

Mima mounds cover a gravel bar in Washtucna Coulee

Upper Grand Coulee with grooved basalt and mima mounds
in the foreground. Steamboat Rock in upper right.

A new theory was born in 1980 after the May 18th Mount St. Helens eruption, when Andrew Berg, a geologist with the U.S. Bureau of Mines in Spokane, Washington, set out to build a dog house. He found that his large piece of plywood had a layer of volcanic ash on it. Using his hammer to dislodge the dust, he noticed that as he pounded on the wood the ash bunched up into uniform little mounds almost equal distance from each other. In contemplating what he was seeing he developed the "Seismic Theory" of mima mound creation.

University students stand atop a mima mound in the
Columbia River Gorge

Mima mounds on otherwise bare basalt scabland at
Horsethief Lake State Park northeast of The Dalles, Oregon

When flying over the channeled scablands, one is struck by the
millions of mima mounds scattered over the scablands. But they
are not just in the northwest, they are a world-wide phenomena and
many theories about their formation. Since this is historical science
and not subject to the normal scientific method of testing and
repeatability, we may never truly know how the mima mounds
came about.

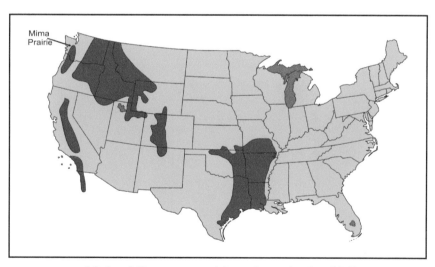

Major Mima mound locations in the U.S.

Panorama photo of Palouse Falls

Perhaps the most iconic view of the channeled Scablands is of Palouse Falls and Lower Palouse Canyon. It leaves an indelible memory for all who do visit this out-of-the-way location 67 miles from Pasco, 101 miles from Spokane, 155 miles from Lewiston, 262 miles from Seattle and 282 miles from Portland.

The dramatic landscape carved by the ice age floods into the brittle and cracked basalt is striking to say the least.

Palouse Falls from the air. The sharp-angled turn of the river is a result of cracks in the basalt bedrock.

Another very dramatic part of the scablands is Frenchman Coulee just 11 miles northeast of Vantage, Washington. It is much as it was the day the GigaFlood stopped flowing.

Dramatic scabland topography in Lower Palouse Canyon

Frenchman Coulee looking northwest toward where it drops
off into the Columbia River

Another view of Frenchman Coulee.
The dark horizontal line in the center is the west bank of the
Columbia River. The gravel bars (left center) were deposited
as the water slowed after the coulee was cut. The boulders,
at the base of the cliff on the right, did not fall from the cliff
but were stranded when the water stopped flowing.

Chapter Six
Water Gaps

There were several constrictions (water gaps) in the flood path that slowed the water causing it to back-up and spread out forming large temporary lakes. When this happened it would leave silt and gravel deposits in the slack-water area behind the narrowing.

I-90 bridge across the Columbia north of Sentinel Gap

Sentinel Gap from the north

The first major constriction was Sentinel Gap where the Columbia River cuts through the Saddle Mountains just south from where the I-90 freeway crosses the Columbia in central Washington. The gap is roughly 1.3 miles wide and about 2.2 miles long.

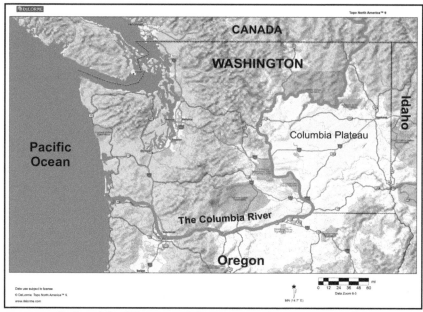

Columbia River and its serpentine route to the
Pacific Ocean

Strandlines on gravel deposits (left center) on the west side
of Sentinel Gap show the height of the flood

Sentinel Gap has sharp edges from being eroded quickly and high water lines on both the east and west side of the gap at about 950 feet above sea level; 460 feet above the waters behind Wanapum Dam. This was the path of only about a third of the GigaFlood. The rest of the water took a more direct route overland toward the major blockage: Wallula Gap.

The Columbia River makes about a 300 degree arc around eastern Washington before cutting sideways through the Horse Heaven Hills and turning abruptly west toward the Pacific Ocean. The place where it cuts through the Hills is called Wallula Gap.

The constriction at Wallula Gap formed a huge lake and backed up water for about 100 miles on the Snake, the Columbia and the Yakima rivers. Geologist have named this temporary lake: Lake Lewis. It covered over 2,000 square miles while waiting to work its way though the gap below the Tri-Cities.

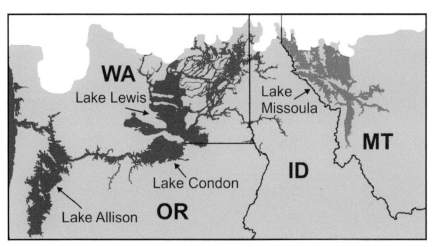

Temporary lakes created by the GigaFlood

Today the gap is slightly over 1 mile wide and 12-1/2 miles long. At the time of the first and largest of the Lake Missoula Floods Wallula Gap was much smaller in width and depth. The abrasion, plucking, kolking and cavitation rapidly widened and deepened this channel through the Hills.

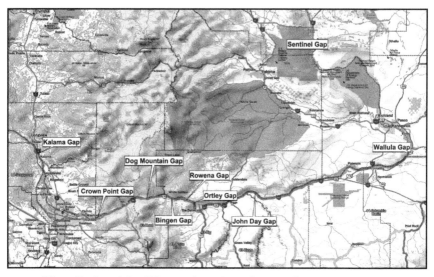

The Columbia River showing the major water gaps

Wallula Gap from the northeast. Twin Sisters are in the
right center of the photograph - Pike Pictures photo

Huge gravel deposit at 950 foot elevation in an overflow
channel on the west side of Wallula Gap

Another overflow, Spring Gulch, on the southeast side of
Wallula Gap, with an 850 foot elevation gravel deposit

The Columbia River Gorge is called a "water gap" because it cuts through a mountain range, but it contains several smaller water gaps. Here are some approximate measurements for the height above present day sea level of the water behind the gaps on the Columbia:

1,250 feet at the Wallula Gap
1,130 feet at the John Day Gap
1,000 feet at the Ortley Gap (today's Columbia Hills)
975 feet at the Rowena Gap
700 feet at the Crown Point Gap
400 feet at the Kalama Gap

Once through Wallula Gap the water spread out and formed a lake; this one behind the John Day Gap and called Lake Condon. Here the water reached over 1,000 feet above sea level and overflowed the banks of the Columbia through several channels into the John Day River before rejoining the Columbia.

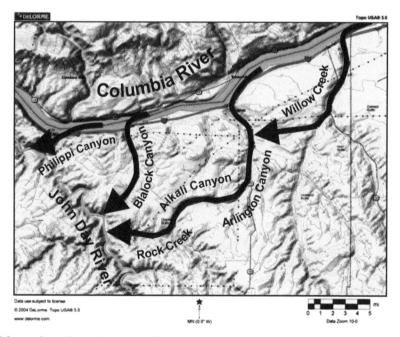

Map showing the overflow channels from the Columbia into the John Day River

Telephoto view looking east through the John Day Gap

The first channel was Willow Creek Canyon which joined the flow from Arlington Canyon to flow through Alkali Canyon and then through Rock Creek into the John Day River. The next was Blalock Canyon and then Philippi Canyon which flowed into the John Day River. In each of these channels we see flood effects that can be called: "scabland topography." These consist of bare scoured rock surfaces, large boulders in unexpected places and gravel deposits.

Almost 670 foot high gravel deposit in former Lake Condon, south of Arlington, Oregon

Columbia River at the mouth of Philippi Canyon overflow
channel with a gravel deposit that is 500 feet high

A closer look at above Philippi Canyon gravel deposit

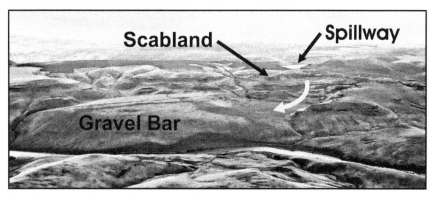

Aerial view from the west of Philippi Canyon. A second huge
gravel mound is left center next to the John Day River.
White arrow shows water flow direction.

Large gravel mine (gray area), approximately 240 feet thick,
on the north side of the Columbia River directly across from
the Fairbanks overflow channel

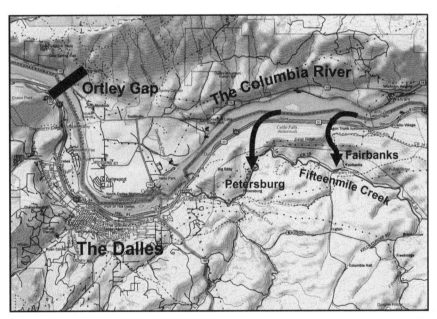

The overflow channels into Fifteenmile Creek northwest of
The Dalles. The water then returned to the Columbia River
by way of Fifteenmile Creek.

East of The Dalles, the water spilled through the Fairbanks and
Petersburg overflow channels into Fifteenmile Creek.

The Fairbanks overflow channel, is enormous. The opening at the Columbia River is about 1,650 feet wide and fans out to over 6,000 feet wide. There is possibly up to 400 feet of gravel, depending on the terrain below the gravel deposit.

Looking southeast across the Columbia River at the Fairbanks overflow channel, east of The Dalles

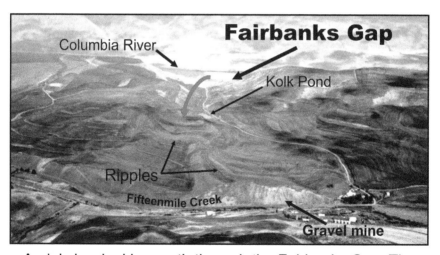

Aerial view looking north through the Fairbanks Gap. The Columbia is barely visible through the notch. Below the notch there are ripple marks and a kolk pond on the top of the deposit. The face of the gravel deposit is in the lower right of the photo. Red arrow shows flow direction.

The Fairbanks gravel deposit from Fifteenmile Road

A tiny portion of the Petersburg gravel deposit

The Petersburg Channel is about two miles wide. It has 300 to 400 feet of gravel in places which has been mined for aggregate with little affect on the amount remaining.

Terraced gravel bar, five miles northwest of The Dalles, deposited as water slowed behind the Ortley Gap

The Ortley Pinnacles part of the Ortley Anticline
(Red line shows tilting of the layers)

The Ortley Gap is west of The Dalles. But the Ortley Anticline is 5.8 miles northwest of The Dalles on the north side of the river. Here faulting has turned the layers on their side and squeezed them until they look like vertical walls or fins.

The Ortley Gap from the west

The Rowena Gap, just eight miles west of The Dalles, backed up water behind it to almost 1,000 feet high and left distinct evidence of being an obstacle to a smooth passage down stream. There are steep cliffs on both sides of the river and scabland topography on the plateaus south of the river. On the north side are gravel beds roughly 250 foot high, one so large that the town of Lyle is built on top of it.

Rowena Gap from the northwest

The floods left a plateau at Rowena, swept it clear of at least two layers of hard basalt lava, and formed kolk ponds at about the 600 foot level. That means that even at that height the floods had enough force to create vortexes that could lift chunks of bedrock and carry them away leaving a water-filled pond in their place.

Today Rowena Crest is part of the Tom McCall Nature Preserve and covered with mima mounds and is gloriously festooned with wildflowers every spring.

Looking north across Rowena Dell and Rowena Crest
to the cliffs on the north side of the river. Note the two
kolk ponds on the finger of land that is Rowena Crest
and the Tom McCall Nature Preserve.

Looking northeast from Rowena Crest at the basalt cliffs
on the north side of the river

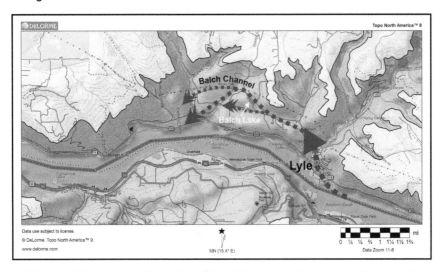

West of Rowena Gap the GigaFlood spilled over the north
bank of the Columbia River and created the Balch Lake
channels and Balch Lake itself

A Lidar map of the Columbia River Gorge shows its many
twists and turns as it snaked through the Cascade
Mountain Range

West of Rowena Gap, the GigaFlood was able to spread out a
bit. It was about 930 feet deep here and moving very fast with a
large load of rock and gravel. On the north side of the river it
found a low spot and scoured out Balch Lake and its channels. It
left gravel deposits on both sides of the Columbia.

Next Cape Horn and Crown Point restricted the massive
turbulent flow increasing it to some of its fastest speed.

Cape Horn cliffs from the air

The 700 foot cliffs at Cape Horn and 600 foot cliffs at Crown Point are a direct result of the flood's power pushing tons of abrasives between the two promontories at freeway speeds.

Water level view of Cape Horn on the north side of the Columbia River

Crown Point from the Washington side of the Columbia River
showing sheared-off face and large landslide on its right
with Rooster Rock on the river's edge (on right)

The last of the water gaps was between Kalama, Washington and Goble, Oregon, 35 miles north of Portland, Oregon. The width of the river today is a little under two miles wide, but at the time of the GigaFlood; it may have been considerably narrower. Some geologists have thought that icebergs from the ice dam had floated all the way down the flood path and were jammed up against Kalama Gap like a huge log jam.

This idea is much like an ice pitcher when the waitress or waiter tries to pour water into your glass. The ice cubes cluster at the spout and slow and perhaps even stops the water from flowing. Little or no water can get through until something "breaks the ice jam."

Without this mechanism, it is a mystery why the opening at Kalama could have caused a back-up large enough to fill the entire Willamette Valley to the 400 foot level.

Whatever the cause of the back-up, water flowing in from the Columbia Gorge at Troutdale accumulated faster than it could flow out through Kalama Gap. This time it filled the Portland-Vancouver basins and then flowed into the Clackamas, Tualatin, Yamhill and Willamette Valleys up to a level of about 400 feet above present day sea level. (See map of Lake Allison page 1).

The lake was named Lake Allison in honor of a 20th century geologist, Ira Allison, who mapped the Willamette Valley locations for no less than 250 erratic boulders larger than 10 inches across. But, at least at first, he thought they were actually glacial erratics and were the product of glacial activity in the Willamette Valley. We now know that there were no glaciers in the valley but there were a lot of icebergs carrying rocks all the way from northern Idaho, Montana and southern Canada where the ice dam has been.

Scientists do not know how long Lake Allison lasted or how many times it filled and emptied. Thomas Condon, Oregon's first official geologist called the area "Willamette Sound" because he thought that at one time it was an arm of the sea. He could tell that the whole valley had been filled with water at some time in the past.

Once the barrier at Kalama Gap broke the floodwater in the valleys of northwest Oregon and southwest Washington were free to forge on to the Pacific Ocean. There they left deposits far out to sea which the ocean currents carried south along the Pacific coast as far as Cape Mendocino, California (400 miles south of the mouth of the Columbia River).

But the most important deposits that they left were the rich soils that average about 150 feet deep in the western valleys of Oregon. This was the treasure for which the Oregon Trail pioneers came to partake. It was this soil that grew the crops that helped feed the California gold seekers and all those who eventually settled and built the west.

Chapter Seven
The Columbia River Gorge

The west end of the Columbia River Gorge from Women's Forum Park on Chanticleer Point. Beacon Rock is in the center background. Cape Horn is on the left and Crown Point with Vista House on the Right.

From the tip of Alaska to the tip of South America there is only one river that cuts through the western mountains. That makes the Columbia River and its gorge a very unique place. It is the only water-level passage from the interior of the continent to the Pacific Ocean and the only slice we have through the western mountains to show us their interior.

When first discovered by Captain Robert Gray, in 1792, it was thought to be the fabled "Northwest Passage," or the "Great River of the West;" a water route from the eastern half of North America to the Pacific Ocean.

The main task given to the Lewis and Clark Corps of Discovery was to locate and determine the feasibility of this valuable trade route. In this, they were disappointed because the eastern tributaries to the mighty Columbia were not navigable and the portage across the Rocky Mountains was too long to be useful. The fact that it was not the "Northwest Passage" does not lessen the geographical significance of the Columbia River Gorge as it cuts through the Cascade Mountain Range.

View of the Gorge down stream from the Mosier tunnels

The Columbia River Gorge cuts sideways across the Cascade Mountain Range. It would have been far easier for the river to find a path south along the eastern side of the Cascades rather than to carve a deep canyon through them. The serpentine path that it takes from its headwaters in Canada would lead one to think that it was a somewhat lazy river taking the easy route wherever possible.

However, when it reached, first, Sentinel Gap, then Wallula Gap and finally the Cascade Mountains it sliced through rather than seek an easier path to the sea, cutting through thousands of feet of hard rock for a space of more than 80 miles.

The river was already here before the GigaFlood both widened and deepened its channel through the mountains. There had been floods before, but nothing like the "big one."

In 1915, the architect of the Columbia River Gorge Scenic Highway, Samuel Lancaster, wrote: "A wall of water tore away the sides and widened the chasm to its present proportions."

This was amazing insight considering that it was 10 years before J Harlen Bretz would submit his conclusions about the "Spokane Flood" in a paper titled "The Channeled Scabland of the Columbia Plateau" in 1923 and another 41 years before this idea was accepted by the geological community.

The present day Columbia River is, by volume, the fourth largest in the United States and the most powerful. It, and its tributaries, account for one-third of all U.S. hydroelectric power and drains an area of 259,000 square miles. Originating in Canada it flows 1,210 miles through British Columbia, Washington and Oregon. The Columbia drains 16 cubic miles of water into the Pacific Ocean every year. During the peak flow of the GigaFlood, it drained that amount in about two hours; as much as 10,000,000 cubic meters per second and in some places rising to over 1,130 feet above sea level. Compare that with the largest flood on the Columbia in historical times; the destructive 1894 flood with a peak discharge of only 34,000 cubic meters per second.

The Columbia River Gorge cuts through about 25 layers of the known 310 lava flows that make up the Columbia River Basalt Group, covering about 163,700 square kilometers (63,200 square miles). Above this the higher peaks are mainly comprised of the Cascade andesite lava that makes up the Cascade Mountains.

When the GigaFlood tore through the gorge it left an erosional remnant: Beacon Rock, 45.5 miles east of Portland. It is easily one of the most recognized landmarks in the gorge. Thought to be the throat of an extinct volcano, it is about 850-feet tall, 437 yards around (¼ mile) and covers 10.5 acres.

Lewis and Clark camped at its base in November of 1805 and again in April 1806. Their journals leave us this written record: "a remarkable high rick [*sic*] about 800 feet high & 400 yds round, the Beaton [*sic*] Rock."

This hard central lava plug had cooled more slowly than the flanks of the volcano and was therefore able to resist the onslaught of ice, boulders and water that roared down the path of the Columbia. When the waters receded what remained was a wide channel with one large punctuation point standing where a mountain had once been.

Beacon Rock from the west

There is a tell-tale flood calling card on the hillside north of Beacon Rock. This is a deposit of rounded river rock which remained after the sides of the volcano were removed.

Beacon Rock was climbed in 1901 to place a banner for a Columbia River steamship company as an advertising stunt. The trail up to the top was first built in 1918 by Henry Biddle. It is now Beacon Rock State Park.

Gravel deposit across Highway 14 from Beacon Rock, left by the GigaFlood

Where the flood waters could spread out they left gravel deposits. Then when forced into a confining section of the Columbia River Gorge the water would speed up. This phenomenon is known as the "venturi effect." The place where it has been calculated to have had the highest velocity is between Cape Horn in Washington and Crown Point in Oregon.

Lewis and Clark calculated the flow of the Columbia to be about one and a half miles per hour. The Mississippi moves at about one mile per hour. A flash flood in a steep mountain ravine can move as fast as 35 mph. The GigaFlood shot through this narrowing of the gorge at speeds of 65 to 80 mph.

The only natural flow that I know of that is faster is a turbidity flow under water or a pyroclastic flow from an erupting volcano which is pushed by steam and other gases from the volcano.

Even if it were just water, moving at freeway speeds it would do incalculable destruction. But this was not just water, it was a slurry of rock, sand and mud resembling the mixture coming out of a cement truck. In mere minutes it could blast away entire hillsides, turning solid rock to dust. This was like a giant sand blaster, reshaping anything it hit.

We know that this is what it was like because of the areas scoured by the floods and by the rock deposits where obstacles allowed parts of the flow to slow enough to drop some of its load.

Looking up from river level
at the 700 foot cliffs of Cape Horn

As a result of the scouring on the Oregon side of the Columbia River Gorge there are 70 waterfalls, the highest concentration of waterfalls in the country. The natural slopes down to the river have been truncated leaving cliffs, hanging valleys (side valleys left stranded above the valley they flow into) and waterfalls. Though there are some waterfalls on the north side of the river most are not as spectacular nor as easily accessible.

Natural bridge in the cliff, (just to the right of the large tree) on the east side of Catherine Creek, a product of the GigaFlood

Coyote Wall (300+ feet high) was a waterfall during the GigaFlood

View north across the Columbia of Table Mountain and Greenleaf Peak; the source of the "Bridge of the gods" landslide, an event long after the ice age floods

Shear basalt cliffs east of Lyle, Washington overtopped
and scoured flat by the GigaFlood

The face was sheared off of Crown Point by the GigaFlood
and Rooster Rock (left of center) was broken off and brought
to river level by a huge landslide

The flat cliff that Multnomah Falls tumbles over as well
as the alcove that it sits in are a result of the GigaFlood

Rowena Crest (left) and Rowena Dell (right) were created
by the fierce erosive power of the GigaFlood slurry.
(View from the north side of the river looking southeast)

Latourell Falls was probably a receding waterfall under
floodwaters more than twice as high as the falls today

Wind Mountain in Washington from the Oregon side
of the Columbia River

Dog Creek Falls on the north side of the Columbia

Catherine Creek waterfall, perhaps less spectacular than some on the Oregon side, but easy to see from a paved wheelchair-accessible trail

The town of Lyle, Washington is built on a Lake Missoula flood gravel deposit

Shellrock Mountain in Oregon viewed from the Washington side of the Columbia River

As the GigaFlood flowed out of the gorge between Camas, Washington and Corbett, Oregon, it spread out, slowed down, and dropped its load of gravel. This formed a massive deposit covering virtually all of the Portland-Vancouver area to a depth of about 300 feet near the mouth of the gorge and tapering toward the north, west and south.

Chapter Eight
Clark County Washington

The first channel that would take the GigaFlood out of the gorge was on the north side; across the river from and just a little east of Crown Point and Rooster Rock State Park. The water rushed around the north side of Mt. Pleasant and Biddle Butte. The water overtopped the ridge north of Biddle Butte, cut the channel now occupied by Canyon Creek and then roared west in the Washougal River Channel.

Cape Horn as seen from Crown Point, showing where the water swept behind Biddle Butte and into the Washougal River Channel

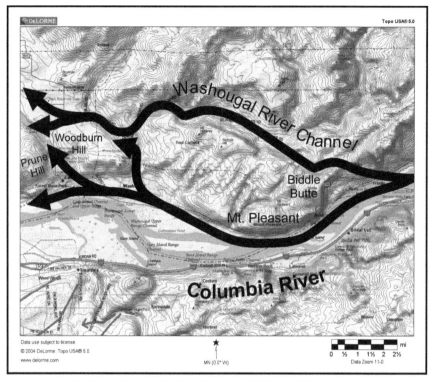

Columbia and Washougal River Channels

Farther downstream at the present sites of Washougal and Camas, with a depth of over 500 feet the GigaFlood surged up the Washougal and Little Washougal Valleys and across a divide, where it flowed behind Woodburn Hill and into the valley of Lacamas Creek.

Another channel formed as it flowed to the northwest, between Prune Hill and the west side of Woodburn Hill, cutting what is now Lacamas Lake. There may have been a small valley or ravine there before the flood. If so, now it was longer, wider and deep enough to hold water after the floodwaters had drained. At some point during this process it cut potholes at the southern end which one can see at Lacamas Park.

The Lacamas Lake that we see today has been enlarged by a man-made dam, but the lake itself was formed by the GigaFlood.

NASA photograph of Columbia River and Lacamas Lake
flood channel (upper right with sun glinting on surface)

Prune Hill from above Highway 14 looking east at the the
south side where it was sheared off. The pre-flood slope
angle would be far more gradual.

Lacamas Lake from high above on western side

Prune Hill felt the full brunt of the blast of ice, water and rock and was severely steepened on its upstream side. This is easily viewed from Highway 14 traveling east from Vancouver to Camas or from the south side of the Columbia between I-205 and Troutdale.

The potholes at the south end of Lacamas Lake

Instead of taking a 90-degree right turn as the Columbia River does now, much of the GigaFlood waters simply headed northwest overland across Clark County forming a number of channels. The main thrust of the river continued west until it hit the West Hills (Tualatin Mountains) where it was forced to turn. This carved out the area that is now filled with Sauvie Island; a huge sand bar left as a by-product of the GigaFlood.

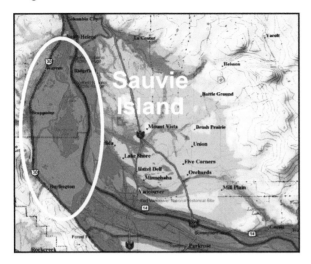

Left:The bend
in the Columbia
River
and Sauvie
Island
(in white oval)

Below:
Clark County
flood channels

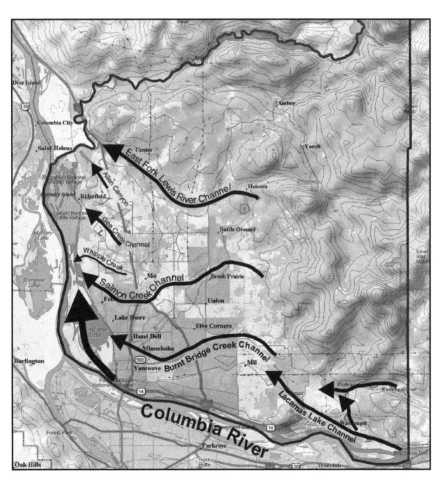

SR 500 follows on the north side of the Burnt Bridge Creek Flood Channel, which roughly parallels the Columbia River Channel. It flows into Cold Canyon (near Hazel Dell) and then into Vancouver Lake. There are several neighborhood parks within the flood channel. This channel flows out of Lacamas Lake and is over 18 miles long, 1,100 feet wide and 140 feet deep in places.

Burnt Bridge Creek Channel from the west

Three miles north of the Burnt Bridge Creek Channel is the Salmon Creek Channel, which flows into Cougar Canyon and Curtis Lake before joining the Columbia River. It is about 12.5 miles long, 2,200 feet wide and 130 feet deep at its mouth.

Salmon Creek Flood Channel, a classic example
of an underfit stream

The largest of the flood channels north of the Columbia is the East Fork Lewis River Channel near La Center, Washington. It is almost too big to photograph but the channel is easily seen as one crosses the bridge into the town of La Center, Washington. It is roughly 10 miles long, 1.4 miles wide and 200 feet deep.

East Fork Lewis River Channel looking east
from the La Center bridge

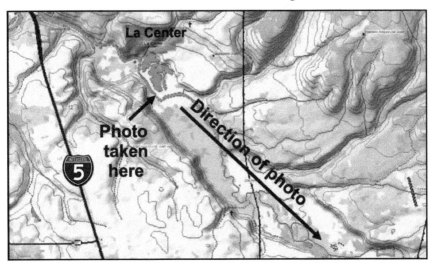

Topographical map of the East Fork Lewis River Channel

The flood channels here are not like the channeled scablands of central Washington in that they are not cut into exposed basalt bedrock. They are simply channels in the gravel deposits laid down by the GigaFlood and the Troutdale gravels beneath them.

The water flowing across the gravels that had just been laid down reached such velocities that it created ripples, like at the beach, but much larger. Throughout Clark County there are stretches where the land undulates in a rhythmical pattern; many of these are actually giant current ripples. The prevailing flow direction was east to west and south to north, and the ripples are found at right angles to the flow directions.

Two rural east/west Clark County roads with ripples

Lincoln Avenue in west Vancouver
with a series of 15 giant current ripples

There are only a few documented ice-rafted boulders in Clark County. This was a geologic puzzle because there should have been many.

The problem found a partial solution in an article in the Spring 2006 *Columbia: The Magazine of Northwest History* called "The Stonecutter and the Missoula Flood Erratics" by Nathan Reynolds.

The author tells about an advertisement in the December 23, 1887 *The LaCamas News* that read: "V. Z. Barthelemy. Dealer in marble and granite. Monuments and Gravestones. Lots inclosed [sic] in granite or soft stone. Also contracts in all kinds of stone-work. All communications addressed to me will receive prompt attention. LaCamas W.T."

LaCamas is now Camas, Washington and Mr. Barthelemy had his business on the slopes of Woodburn Hill where there is no natural source of granite. He apparently was gathering Clark County erratics and cutting them for use as building stones and monuments.

Records do not show where most of his stones were put to use, but we do know where one is. On Thursday, July 31, 1884, the *Vancouver Independent* ran an article under the headline, "Impos-ing Ceremony," which described the laying of the cornerstone of the new cathedral in Vancouver.

". . . the cornerstone, a huge beautiful granite 36x24x18 inches, quarried, dressed and presented by Mr. Bartholomy [sic] of LaCa-mas, W.T., where the stone is found, ..."

It can be seen today on the southwest corner of St. James Catholic Church at: 218 West 12th Street, Vancouver, WA 98660

The cornerstone has this Latin inscription: "This temple of God was built under the great Pontiff Leo XIII and Aegidius Junger, II Bishop of Nesqually In the year of our Lord 1884.

Chapter Nine
Gravel Pits and Rock Quarries

After exiting the Lacamas Lake Channel, the water quickly spread out and met with waters that had taken other paths. Again it slowed down and dropped much of its gravel. The larger rocks and gravel had not come through that narrow channel but millions of tons of small gravel and sand had. The English Pit (one of many rock pits in the area) is about 1.2 square miles just northwest of the upper end of Lacamas Lake. As of this writing, the pit was 75 feet deep and not yet down to bedrock. They have removed an enormous amount of gravel from this pit and have actually built a shopping center and housing complex within part of it.

Looking north across the English Pit
(named for homesteaders in the area)

Foreset beds in the English Pit dipping north

The gravel layers dip from south to north in what is called foreset bedding, indicating a rapidly moving gravel bar with the gravel being pushed over the top and down the down-stream side of the bar. At the area of the quarry, this gravel bar was over three and one-half miles wide and over nine miles long. It was formed in the flood shadow of Prune Hill (an area where the hill caused the water to slow and drop much of its cargo).

Another section of the English Pit shows the wave action of very turbulent flood waters

On the west side of Prune Hill is a gravel pit visible for miles especially from the Oregon side of the Columbia River. Quarries and rock pits are usually located where it is easy to access and remove rock. Floodwaters expose bedrock by the removal of topsoil and/or deposit gravel in large quantities of smaller-sized rocks. In this gravel pit the GigaFlood did both. The flood ripped away the topsoil exposing the columnar basalt on the side of the hill and deposited sedimentary gravels in a depression near the top of the gravel pit site.

The mile-long Fisher Pit from the Oregon side of the River

The Fisher Rock Pit with Columbia River Basalt overlaid by flood gravels

On the north side of the Lewis River Flood Channel is a small sand pit where slower water dropped a load of sand and silt without any gravel to speak of at all. This was a slack-water area where the sand could settle out of very slow moving water.

The author examines the way sand was deposited - Sylvia Thompson photo

Sand pit in the East Fork Lewis River Channel with foreset beds dipping to the northwest. Several gravel layers on top of the sand indicate that the water velocity sped up

Tebo Rock Pit

The "Tebo Pit," on the south rim of the East Fork Lewis River flood channel was worked for many years. There was 20 feet of overburden on top of the 130 feet of medium to coarse gravel (3½ inches or less with some cobbles). This particular rock pit was 100 feet deep at the time it was being mined-out and closed.

Another rock pit is the Lewisville Pit at the east end of the East Fork Lewis River Channel. This is part of a massive gravel deposit with foreset beds dipping to the north and west.

North wall of the Lewisville Pit with gravel dipping to the west at a steep angle

West wall of the Lewisville Pit shows a northward dip to the gravel deposit

The total amount of gravel laid down north of the Columbia between the gorge outlet and the narrows at Kalama is truly beyond comprehension. South of the Columbia River, an equal or greater amount was deposited between Corbett and Oregon City.

East Portland has very similar gravels underlying most of its streets. Once in awhile road building or other construction projects will open the face of the ground and give us a peak at what is beneath. A road cut at NE 82nd and Broadway showed almost identical foreset bedding as those in Clark County.

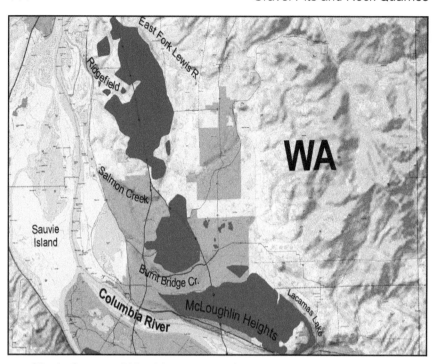

Clark County Washington; red areas show deep gravel deposits

Looking south at foreset bedding in road cut
at NE 82nd and Broadway
in Portland (close-up below)

Chapter Ten
Portland Area Inundation

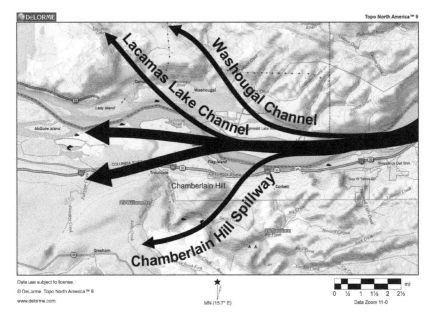

The flood channels into Portland and Vancouver. Note the Chamberlain Hill spillway where it overflowed the ridge between the Columbia and the Sandy rivers.

The water, mud, rocks and ice of the GigaFlood began to reach what is now the Portland-Vancouver area at the west end of the Columbia River Gorge within hours after the breaking of the ice dam on the Clark Fork River.

If you had been on high ground (800 feet or so above sea level) you could have heard the roar and felt the blast of wind that preceded the water by about a half hour. If you were not on high ground, you probably would not have heard the sound and the 30-

minute warning would probably have been of very little use, even if you could have understood what it meant.

Though not as narrow as Wallula Gap, the gap at the west end of the gorge did cause the water to rise to over 700 feet deep at Crown Point and at least 540 feet at Corbett. As it flowed out of the gorge, it immediately fanned out into what geologists call the Portland Delta.

A delta is formed when a stream's velocity slows as it flows into a standing body of water such as a lake or ocean. Here it created its own lake by filling up the Portland-Vancouver area as well as the entire Willamette Valley. (See Lake Allison map pg. 1)

View from Troutdale of Broughton's Bluff on the northwest side of Chamberlain Hill; a favorite of rock climbers

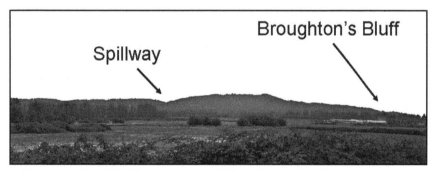

Chamberlain Hill from north of the Columbia River showing the spillway where water went around the east side of the Hill into the Sandy River (Bluff hidden by trees at right)

On the south side of the Columbia River Gorge the flood swept over the 700 foot high crest of Crown Point and sheared off the 600 foot cliffs. Just four miles west of Crown Point it cut across the divide to the south into the Sandy River Valley on the east side of Chamberlain Hill. On the northwest side of Chamberlain Hill it scoured away the river side of the hill creating the cliffs we now call Broughton's Bluff. Then spread out and covered the entire Portland area to a depth of 400 feet.

Looking southwest down the Chamberlain Hill spillway

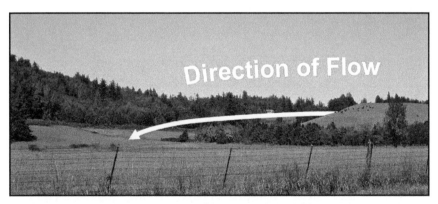

South end of spillway on Chamberlain Hill looking north. The water came from behind the hill on the right to flow toward camera position. It then flowed down over the edge into the Sandy River Valley.

Lidar map of
Chamberlain Hill
(center) with the
spillway in red.
Sandy River is on
the west side.

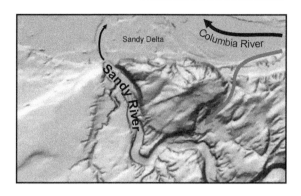

As the water cut over this ridge west of Corbett and dropped off into the Sandy River Valley, it backed up the Sandy River to just north of the town of Sandy. This point of the river can be seen atop the 466 foot cliffs at the Jonsrud View Point on Bluff Road just northeast of Sandy High School. The bluff was probably created, not by the GigaFlood, but by the circa 1800 eruption of Mount Hood that sent torrents of water, mud and volcanic ash down the Sandy River and out into the Columbia much like what happened on the Toutle River following the 1980 Mt. St. Helens eruption. It was the volcanic ash from this eruption that added to the sand bar at the mouth of the Sandy River that led Lewis and Clark to give it the name: "Quicksand River," after they almost lost a man in the shifting sand; much of which has eroded away now.

As the flood water level began to lower it channelized around the largest gravel deposits and obstacles such as Rocky Butte, Mt. Scott and others of the Boring Volcanoes. In the channels it was able to speed up again and move much of the sediments that it had just deposited. These pathways are still visible today.

East Portland received an extraordinary amount of rock and gravel carried downstream by the GigaFlood. The largest of the rocks seem to have been dropped here instead of north of the Columbia. After the flood had released much of its 50 cubic miles of rocky accumulation, it started reincorporating some of it and moving it farther downstream. The newly formed Portland Delta became a bit of an obstacle for the remaining waters of the flood which then started to form channels where it could speed up and cut through some of the mounds of gravel. Between channels, it left the gravel bars that east Portland is built on.

The water from the mouth of the Columbia flowed northwesterly across Clark County but in Portland it flowed southwesterly.

The shapes of the gravel bars indicate the direction of flow because gravel was left on the downstream side of immoveable hills. In some cases the bar became a double bar trailing behind the obstruction that caused it.

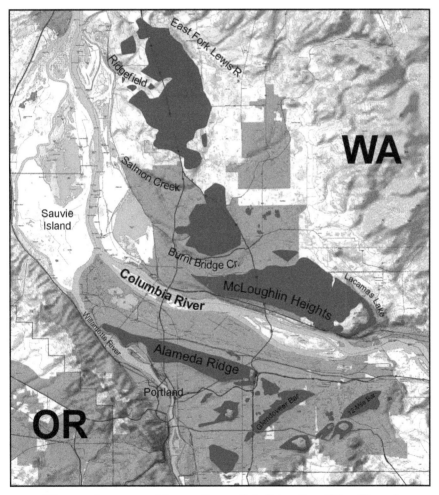

The major gravel bars (in red) left by the GigaFlood
in Portland and Vancouver

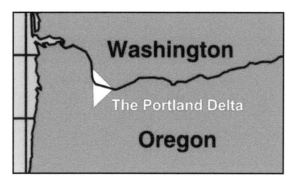

The location of
the Portland
Delta

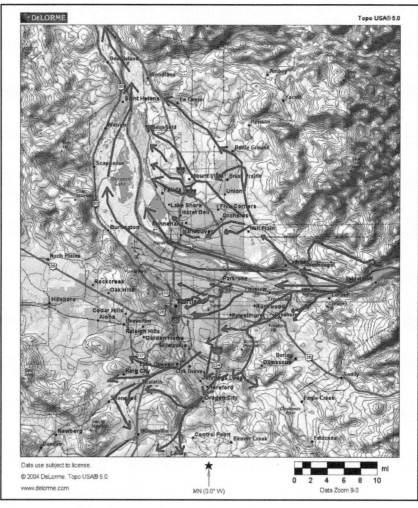

Topographical map showing how the channelized waters
flowed into and through the Portland Delta

One of the large gravel bars is over 5 miles long, about 300 feet high, and a little over 1 mile at its widest point. The top of this gravel bar is now the site of the Glendoveer Golf Course. It stretches from the area of 174th and Glisan all the way to 82nd Avenue and Holgate Blvd. Boulders, about the size of small cars close to the mouth of the gorge, diminish in size farther west.

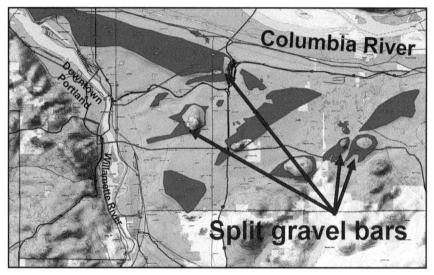

Obstacles with double gravel bars trailing on the downstream side

The gravel bar west of Rocky Butte: Alameda Ridge, used to continue some 14 miles, all the way from Rocky Butte to the West Hills (Tualatin Mountains) and briefly blocked the Willamette River but the west end was cut off by the exiting floodwaters. To get a good view of the size of this gravel bar drive north on NE 72nd Avenue across the golf course to NE Sacramento Street.

Most of the rocks and huge boulders transported in the GigaFlood were Columbia River Basalt; the bedrock covering much of the region. These were transported either from eastern Washington or from the Columbia River Gorge. These are not glacier or iceberg erratics. The term erratic only refers to rocks that have no local source.

Granite is not native to the Willamette Valley so any granite rocks, not transported for industrial or personal reasons, are known immediately to be erratics.

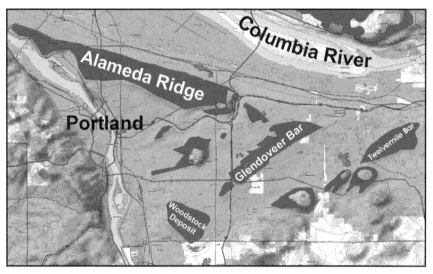

The largest gravel bars in Portland

Some of the largest rocks in east Portland

The Thai brothers having a rocky
afternoon in northeast Portland

Most construction sites in east Portland end up with a big
pile of rocks like this one

Airborne kids having fun with rocks on Columbia Boulevard
in northeast Portland

Mark Buser with large pile of flood rocks removed from an
industrial park

Sometimes these rocks can be a real challenge

This car-size Missoula flood boulder is about halfway up the
east side of Rocky Butte in northeast Portland

Many yards in east Portland have large rocks
in their landscaping

"Jack-O-Rock"

Chapter Eleven
Portland Area Flood Channels

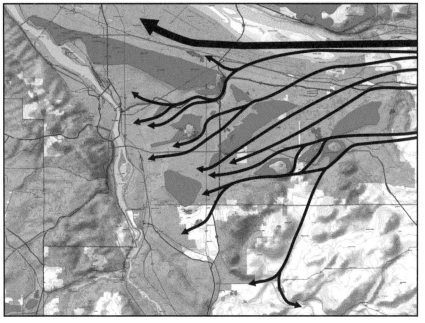

Map of east Portland showing most of the
incoming flood channels

As stated previously, water slows when it spreads out and speeds up when it is confined to a narrow channel. When it flowed around rocky hills, it cut deep channels. You can see this on the beach when water flows around a rock leaving a channel in the sand on each side where the water sped up and flowed around the rock or between two rocks if they are close enough.

Rocky Butte, an extinct volcano near the mouth of the gorge, felt the full force of the GigaFlood. After tearing away the north and east flanks of the volcano the water then gouged a deep ravine on the east side. It then left two gravel bars: Alameda Ridge on the northwest and a smaller bar on the southwest side.

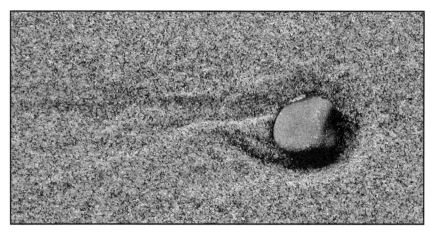

Beach rock showing erosion pattern very similar to what happened at Rocky Butte on a much larger scale during the GigaFlood. (Water flow from right to left).

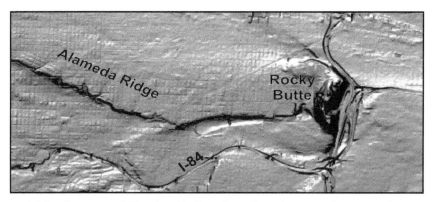

Lidar image of Rocky Butte showing depressions on the west and the east side. (Water flow from right to left).

Between these two gravel bars there used to be a lake, which was drained over 100 years ago. Now a deep depression stretches from Rocky Butte to about 60th Avenue. This is most visible in the Rose City Golf Course on 72nd Avenue between Tillamook and Sacramento. The low area is also visible on both sides of 82nd Avenue just north of I-84. Another good view is to drive on NE Fremont Drive between NE 83rd Avenue and NE 92nd Avenue.

On 82nd across from Madison High School there was a gravel pit which was later converted to a landfill. While it was an active pit one could have seen the foreset bedding laid down by the GigaFlood. On the north side of the pit the beds dipped to the south and on the south side they dipped to the north showing how the gravel was pushed around Rocky Butte and then laid down in the north and south gravel bars leaving a depression between them.

Some say this depression was a plunge pool caused by the waters flowing over the top of Rocky Butte, but I disagree. The butte is 15 miles west of Troutdale and Washougal where the floodwaters left the restriction of the gorge and quickly spread out from about one mile to almost 16 miles wide and dropped from a depth of 600 feet to 400 feet. Very little water could have gone over the 460-foot saddle and the water that did would have landed in water that had flowed around the butte not hitting the ground hard enough to gouge out a plunge pool. A receding waterfall cutting into a ridge of bedrock forms plunge pools; hills do not.

This depression is in sedimentary deposits and there is no evidence of a waterfall. I believe that this depression is simply an area protected from receiving gravel that swept around the butte. There was a clay deposit in the depression area that was mined for bricks. Since clay is a very fine sedimentary deposit, I think the best explanation for the clay is that this was a sheltered slack water area between the channels during the flood.

Panoramic view of the cliffs on the northeast corner of Rocky Butte. The view is from the direction of the flow.

Flowing south of Rocky Butte and north of Mount Tabor the water cut a channel, now occupied by the I-84 freeway and the tracks of both the railroad and the MAX Light Rail commuter train. Known since pioneer days as Sullivan's Gulch, it is still about 60 feet deep at the 12th Avenue overpass near Lloyd Center. It was considerably deeper before sedimentation and urbanization filled the bottom.

Aerial view of Rocky Butte (looking to the southwest). Note the channel on the left side cut by the GigaFlood

Sullivan's Gulch looking west from the 12th Avenue overpass toward downtown Portland

Driving I-84 or viewing it on a map will show a gentle "S" curve north and east of Mount Tabor. This was caused by the backwash of water from Mount Tabor, which joined with the Sullivan's Gulch water and cut the curve we see today.

Some of the water spilled south out of Sullivan's Gulch and cut through the Laurelhurst Park area gouging out and leaving the small lake that is the focal point of the park. The lake is linear and stretches from the northeast to the southwest. That is because it is part of the flood channel that flowed through east Portland.

Sullivan's Gulch looking east from the 12th Avenue
overpass.

One of the flood channels flowed west and south of Grant
Butte in east Portland. Division Street crosses it at NW Birdsdale
Avenue. It met a channel coming in from the east through
Gresham that turned west toward Powell Butte. In 1902 The
Oregon Water Power & Railway Company utilized this channel for
its right-of-way. It has been transformed into the Springwater
Corridor; a paved public walking and bicycle trail and a fun way to
see the bottom of a flood channel. It stretches 16 miles from near
the town of Boring to the Willamette River in Sellwood and
connects with other trails that make up a 40-mile loop.

The water skirted Powell Butte on the south and due to its
increased speed cut a deep canyon between Powell Butte, Scouter
Mountain and Walter's Hill. Johnson Creek now follows the
course of this channel; but the GigaFlood, not Johnson Creek, cut
the ravine. There are several small lakes, ponds and wetlands in the
Johnson Creek Channel that have not completely silted in since the
time of the flood.

In southeast Portland while the flood was at its deepest, some
of the water diverted through a channel south of Powell Butte now
known as Pleasant Valley. That water continued south down Rock
Creek, joining water flowing in through the Carver Gap and filling
the Clackamas River Valley all the way to the outskirts of
Estacada.

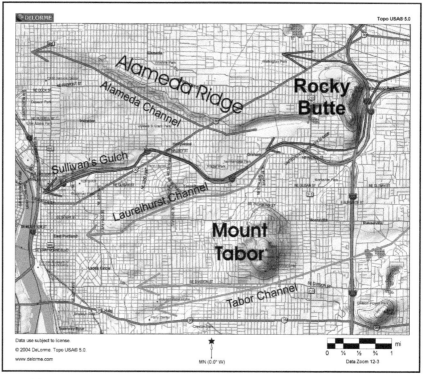

Map showing the Alameda Channel, Sullivan's Gulch
Channel, Laurelhurst Channel, and Tabor Channel

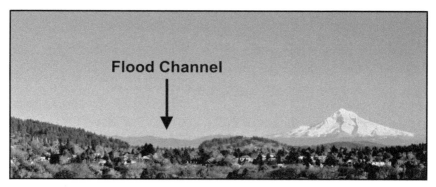

Photo taken from the Marquam Bridge showing the Tabor
flood channel between Mount Tabor (left) and Kelly Butte
(center). Notice how the sides next to the channel are
steeper than those on the opposite side of the hills.
Mount Hood on the right.

The water filled the Portland-Vancouver basin within an hour or two of flowing out of the gorge. However, as a funnel filling too fast, the water had to find somewhere else to go. It went south into the Clackamas, Tualatin and Willamette valleys.

The GigaFlood hit Portland's West Hills (Tualatin Mountains) and because it could not overtop them it then flowed both north and south. The West Hills average about 1,000 feet in elevation, which made an impenetrable barrier for the 400-foot deep floodwaters.

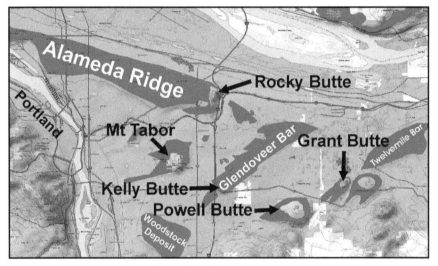

East Portland buttes

However, eight miles south of Portland a ravine provided an avenue for the flood to enter the Tualatin Valley thus cutting Lake Oswego. The flood then rushed through this gap and filled the Tualatin Valley as far as Gales Creek, almost 30 miles west of Portland.

At roughly the same time as it was bursting through the Lake Oswego Gap, it found another outlet to the east where the Clackamas River had cut through the hills at Carver. The water poured through Carver Gap, enlarging it both as it flowed in and again as it flowed back out at the end of the flood.

At the south end of the Portland basin, the flood found another outlet, the Oregon City Gap, where the Willamette River cut through a ridge of basalt. Floodwater ripped through this gap into the Willamette Valley with tremendous power bringing rocks and icebergs with it. It left tall cliffs on both sides of the Willamette River for a stretch of five and a half miles.

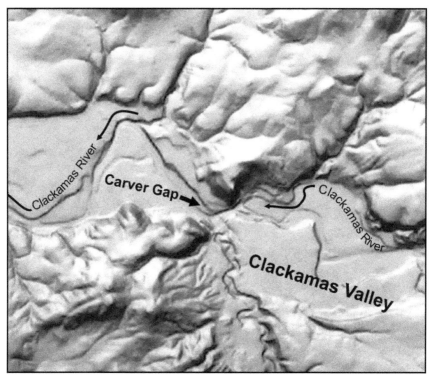

Lidar map of the Carver Water Gap

The Carver Gap looking southeast from Highway 212 railroad overpass. Mount Hood on left.

The Carver Gap from the southwest

The torrent of floodwaters pouring through the Oregon City Gap left a very large fan-shaped gravel deposit where the town of Canby, Oregon is today.

The Oregon City Gap (top left) and Willamette Falls (bottom center)

Water level view of the 50 foot drop at Willamette Falls

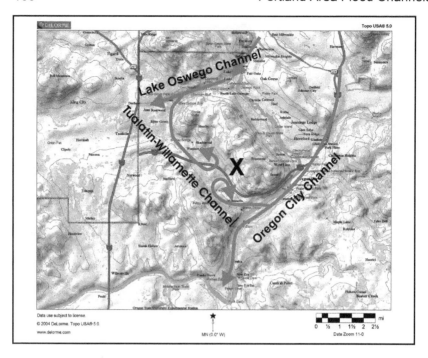

Location of the Tualatin-Willamette channel.
X marks the approximate location where the Willamette
Meteorite was found. Arrows show the water direction and
the eddy at lower end of channel that created the bar.

The GigaFlood waters filled the area where I-205 now passes
between West Linn and Tualatin. I call this the Tualatin-
Willamette channel. The water may have briefly flowed one
direction, then reversed, and flowed the opposite direction.

Most of the water going through the Oregon City Gap flowed
into the Willamette Valley. But part split and flowed northwest
into the Tualatin-Willamette channel causing an eddy to form that
dropped a huge amount of gravel in a bar just north of what is now
the mouth of the Tualatin River.

The historic West Linn neighborhood of Willamette sits on this
hill. What remains today of this gravel bar is about one and three
quarters mile long, half a mile wide and roughly 200 feet above the

present river level. Fields Bridge Park, with its interpretive kiosks dedicated to the ice age floods story, is at the west end of this bar.

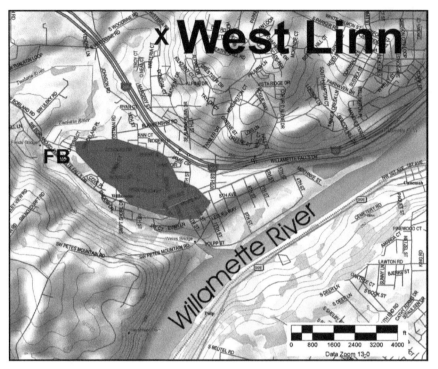

Red area marks the Willamette gravel bar. Black **X** marks the approximate location where the Willamette Meteorite was found. **FB** marks the location of Field's Bridge Park

There is a picturesque scabland on a ridge on the northeast side of the river that was overtopped by the flood as it flowed through the Oregon City Gap. It swept away parts of at least three lava flows leaving kolk ponds, knobs and bare rock. This is the Camassia Nature Preserve in West Linn. The blue/purple Camas lily, for which the preserve was named, flowers abundantly in the spring, and was a food staple for the indigenous peoples. The rare White Rock Larkspur (*Delphium leucophaeum*) is also found there.

A very similar scabland, Canemah, is on the east side of the Willamette River just south of, and high above, Willamette Falls.

Camassia in springtime with the Camas flower in bloom

Camassia in the summer when the lack of soil causes
much of it to go brown

Canemah scabland in Oregon City

Bare rock and the Willamette River from Canemah

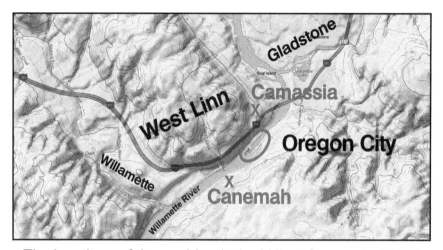

The locations of the scablands (red X) at Camassia (West Linn) and Canemah (Oregon City). Red oval marks Willamette Falls

On the east side of the Cascades, the lack of rainfall has left the scablands essentially as they were the day after the flood. However, west of the mountains, 40 to 60 inches of annual rainfall has added soil, vegetation and erosion. Camassia, quite a unique place, is on a high terrace where many rocks are still exposed. It is well worth a visit for its stark beauty, geologic significance, wildlife viewing and enjoyable walking trails.

As the water slowed, it lost much of its carrying capacity except for the fine silt that it carried as far west as McMinnville, as far east as Estacada and as far south as Eugene. This water-borne silt gave the Willamette Valley its unique fertile quality. This silt can be traced nearly to the 400 foot level which was the highest level reached by the floodwaters. There is a noticeable change in soil color, and in some cases vegetation, near that elevation.

The Willamette silt is very much like the Palouse loess from which it is derived. The major difference is the sandy brown color due to a few more minerals from the basalt and other rocks that were broken up, transported and mixed with it by the flood. It makes very fertile farm soil throughout the valleys of northwestern Oregon.

Chapter Twelve
Erratic Boulders

Bellevue Erratic

The GigaFlood was all about ice. Ice caused the 40 square mile obstruction, allowing Glacial Lake Missoula to form. When broken up, the ice carried rocks that acted as water-driven battering rams to help abrade the channeled scablands, the Columbia River Gorge and the Portland area channels.

Ice may have played a role in reinforcing the hydraulic dams that formed the periodic lakes at narrow places in its path. In addition, icebergs rafted the erratic boulders that mark where the flood had been.

The erratics here are recognized because they are not composed of basalt lava which is the main type of rock found in this area. Most of the erratics are granite or metamorphosed sedimentary rocks from the northern Rocky Mountains in northern Idaho, northwestern Montana, or even southern Canada. This means that they are called "exotic erratics" because they are made up of a rock type that does not occur naturally anywhere near where the rock is found.

While the ice dam was forming some rocks simply fell from the mountainsides onto the top of mountain glaciers and got a free ride down the ravine on the back, or buried within, the glacier until it became part of the ice lobe and eventually an iceberg when the dam broke. Others were plucked from the steep valley sides and bottom by the glaciers and rode the rest of the way inside the ice. Some erratics show gouge marks and striations from where they were scraped along by the glacier. Others are rounded from being rolled at some point during its journey.

If the glacier ends in a body of water, the glacier breaks or "calves" off icebergs. Any rocks on or within those icebergs are transported wherever that iceberg travels. When the iceberg becomes grounded in shallow water, it melts leaving its cargo of rocks and boulders. These are found distributed widely within the channeled scablands and anywhere the waters of the GigaFlood took them.

The largest Willamette Valley erratic is the "Bellevue Erratic" found at the Erratic Rock State Natural Site near McMinnville, Oregon at 306 feet above sea level. It is close to 100 tons of argillite, a metamorphosed mud stone, said to be the largest piece of argillite outside of Canada.

A news article came out in 2001 claiming that the Bellevue Erratic was disappearing. The original weight in the 1950's was calculated at 160 tons and now it is said to be down to 90 tons. If ones does the math that means that 70 tons walked away in just over 50 years – that would be a little over 1-1/3 tons a year. I find it hard to believe but I sincerely hope no one would take pieces of it for any reason.

I am firmly convinced that it is virtually the same as it was when it as photographed for Ralph Friedman's "Oregon for the Curious" which shows it to be almost identical to how it looks today. For comparison, I restaged his photograph and I can see no change from then until now.

Photo taken in the late 60s or early 70s
(Courtesy of *Oregon for the Curious*, 1972, by Ralph Friedman, published by Caxton Press)

Photo of Bethany Janzen in 2009 (Ron Crowl photo)

There are many other erratics around western Oregon and southwest Washington, but as time goes on the numbers are diminishing because they are moved, buried or destroyed by industry and urbanization. Fortunately, many are now preserved in parks and featured in landscapes.

Perhaps the most famous exotic erratic found in the Willamette Valley is also the one that has traveled farther than all the rest. What is now known as the Willamette Meteorite was once just an exotic erratic boulder resting on a hillside southeast of Portland.

In 1902 Ellis Hughes, a former Welsh miner working as a wood cutter, found it on his neighbor's property near West Linn and spent three months moving it to his property.

Sign advertising the
Willamette Meteorite

Ellis Hughes' barn for
displaying the meteorite

There he built a barn for the meteorite and charged 25 cents a piece for people to view it. It didn't take long for his neighbor, Oregon Iron and Wire Company, to notice the crude road he had built to move the huge rock from their land to his and realize that the meteorite was originally theirs.

After several lengthy court battles, all the way to the Supreme Court of the United States, it was determined that it belonged to the owners of the land where it was found.

Ellis Hughes' wooden cart used to move the meteorite.
Ellis Hughes is not shown in this photo
(Courtesy Oregon Historical Society, Image #58662)

It was put on auction and sold for $26,000.00; then donated to the American Museum of Natural History in New York City where it is displayed as the Willamette Meteorite. The 1905 Lewis and Clark Centennial Exposition was the last time it was seen in Oregon though various groups over the last 100 years have unsuccessfully tried to get it back.

In structure it is a metallic nickel-iron meteorite, weighing over 15.5 tons. It is the largest meteorite ever found in the United States and the sixth largest meteorite in the world. It is also the largest "oriented meteorite" ever found. This means that it apparently did not tumble as it came through the atmosphere. This is what gives it the classic "space capsule" look.

It is not known for sure that it is an erratic. However, there was no crater where it was found and other rocks around it were determined to be erratics. Also, it was found resting in an area where there was a large eddy in the floodwaters making it a likely spot for an iceberg to become grounded.

The meteorite arriving at the American Museum of Natural History in New York City. Note that the weight of the rock is causing the right rear wagon wheel to sink into the pavement
(Image # 45633 American Museum of Natural History Library)

The Willamette Meteorite as originally displayed in the American Museum of Natural History
(Image # 2a13517 American Museum of Natural History Library)

If this is the case, the meteorite probably landed on a glacier in southern Canada or perhaps the ice lobe itself, traveled with the ice lobe and ended up in an iceberg when the ice dam broke. It then traveled the next 500 miles trapped in an iceberg that grounded, melted and deposited the rock at the 380 foot level on a hillside in West Linn.

About two miles south of where the Willamette Meteorite was found, the City of West Linn has a model on display at 14th Street and Willamette Falls Drive.

Willamette Meteorite display in West Linn, Oregon

There is a one-fifth scale exact replica of the meteorite as part of the ice age floods interpretive walk along the Tualatin River at Fields Bridge Park in West Linn. There are also three large granite erratics at the beginning of the interpretive walk.

The following photos illustrate just some of the interesting erratics in our region.

Fields Bridge Park kiosk and Willamette meteorite replica

Granite erratics in Fields Bridge Park

Clackamas Community College granite erratic

The largest of over 25 erratics found on the grounds of
Left Coast Cellars on 99W north of Rickreall, Oregon

Granite erratic found nearby is part of the landscaping at
Lane Community College in Eugene, Oregon

Maryhill Museum of Art near Goldendale, Washington,
has two erratics on the museum grounds

Rex Hill Winery has this erratic displayed near their tasting
room on 99W just east of Newberg, Oregon

This granite erratic, on Wallace Road, NW of Salem, was
used for a memorial to George Cay who died in 1882; the
builder of the first brick house west of the Rocky Mountains

Erratic hunter, Jeff Murray, and Sylvia Thompson rest on an
erratic boulder found in the Yamhill Valley near Baskett
Slough, west of Salem

Washington State University, Vancouver campus, has this
large granite erratic that was moved from a nearby
housing tract

Granite erratic (left) and an andesite flood rock (right) in
front of business in Gresham, Oregon

Mica filled granite erratic in rural cemetery

This granite erratic (lower left), discovered in 2011, is located at the Kaiser Permanente Westside Medical facility in Hillsboro where it is displayed with a brass plaque and two bronze beavers for companions

These boulders are called erratics because they do not have a local source and have been moved from their original location. Many of them have been moved several times since their deposition by the floodwaters and some are still being moved today. We hope they will be preserved and available for viewing when their restlessness is complete.

Chapter Thirteen
Tualatin, Yamhill and Willamette Valleys

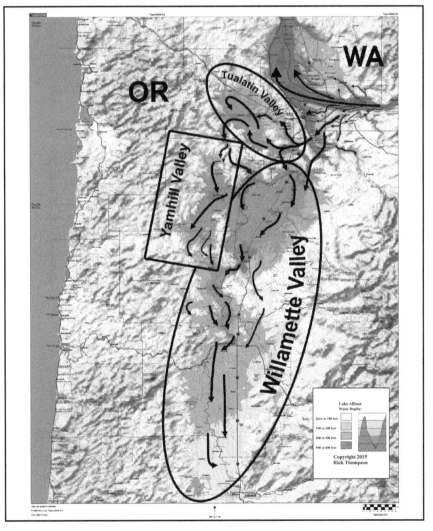

Three valleys of western Oregon that felt the effects of the
GigaFlood. Arrows indicate incoming flow directions

As the GigaFlood burst out of the Columbia River Gorge, it filled up the Portland basin and spilled out into the Clackamas (southeast of Portland), Tualatin (west of Portland), Yamhill (southwest of Portland), and Willamette (south of Portland) Valleys. The floodwaters filled each of these valleys to almost 400 feet above today's sea level.

Oregon City Gap from the north where the flood entered directly into the Willamette Valley. Water also entered through the Tualatin and Yamhill Valleys

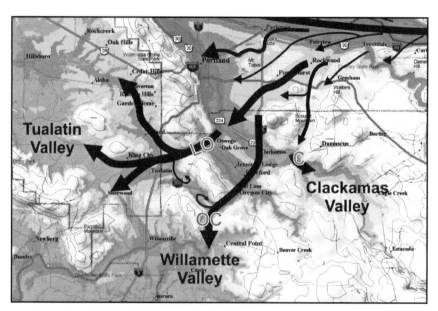

The flood flowed through Portland into the Clackamas, Tualatin and Willamette Valleys. The water gaps are: (in red) "C"=Carver, "LO"=Lake Oswego and "OC"=Oregon City

The massive force of water enlarged the existing stream channels modifying the Carver, Lake Oswego, and the Oregon City gaps. The Lake Oswego Gap is almost a direct shot from the mouth of the Columbia River Gorge with few obstacles in its way. Geologists once believed this was the original bed of the Tualatin River. There surely was a canyon with some kind of stream in it. When the floodwaters hit, it reversed the stream's flow and made it the main channel out of the Portland basin.

The Oregon City Gap is two miles farther from the gorge and has obstacles that would slow the rampaging waters before reaching it. Also, it is narrower and longer than the Lake Oswego Gap further restricting the flow out of the Portland basin. This meant, at least at the beginning, the Lake Oswego Channel carried more water than the Oregon City Channel.

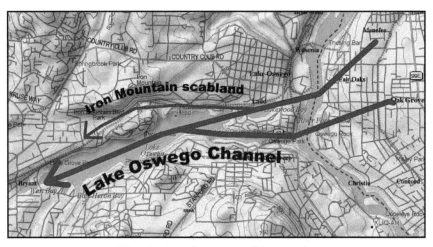

The Lake Oswego Channels

Squeezing through the Lake Oswego Gap it sped up, similar to the way water from of a garden hose speeds up as you close down the nozzle, eroding the sides and bottom of the channel. The erosion worked backwards in the east to west water flow. The erosion started at the west end of the channel, near today's Bridgeport Village shopping center, and progressed east.

Lake Oswego from the northeast looking to the southwest in
the same direction as the water was flowing

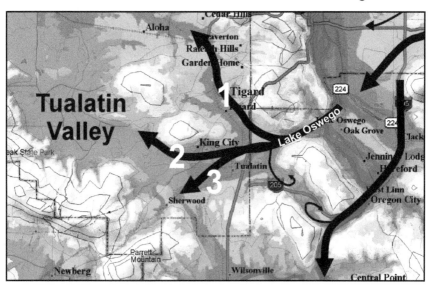

The Lake Oswego Channel split into three channels that
flowed into the Tualatin Valley: (1) Tigard-Beaverton
Channel, (2) Durham-King City Channel and (3) Tualatin-
Sherwood Channel.

The force of the water ripped rocks out of their place, weakened the upstream rocks allowing them to be removed, and created a channel similar to the way receding waterfalls are formed. This headward erosion eventually opened up this area to nearly half a mile wide and over 350 feet deep leaving a basin for today's Lake Oswego. There are two channels there, but only one was deep enough to continue holding water. The Iron Mountain channel is now a residential part of the town of Lake Oswego.

The west end of Lake Oswego (now mostly shopping centers) where the water broke through the West Hills (Tualatin Mountains) and spread out to form a delta (white lines outline delta) of sand and gravel

Mark Buser with flood rock torn out of Lake Oswego and dropped in what is now a residential area just west of the lake - Charles Hall Photo

Once into the Tualatin Valley the water slowed down dropping millions of tons of rock in a delta at the west end of Lake Oswego ranging from huge boulders down to gravel and then sand and silt. These gravel deposits were mined for over 100 years. The largest of the rock pits was in the Durham area and now is the home of the Bridgeport Village shopping center.

The heavy load of gravel began to fill up the channel directly to the west of Lake Oswego causing the water to divert into three smaller channels. One went north through Tigard and Beaverton into the Tualatin Valley; the second went straight west through Durham and passed King City. The third channel cut southward through the Nyberg Greenway and into downtown Tualatin and Sherwood.

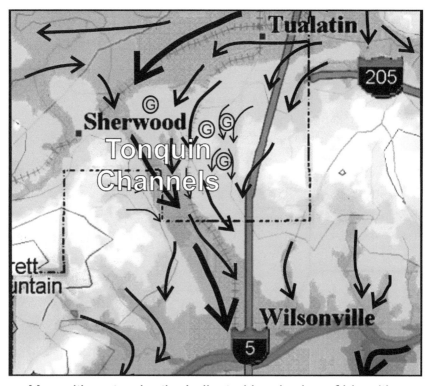

Map with water depths indicated by shades of blue (the darkest being the deepest). Arrows show the direction of the water flow through Tualatin and the Tonquin Scablands ("G" indicates gravel deposits)

Old wooden train trestle crossing the main Tonquin Channel

Another view (looking North) of the old electric train trestle
going over the Tonquin flood channel

The main Tonquin flood channel looking south from
SW Oregon Street in Sherwood

Coffee Lake, a kolk pond within the Tonquin flood channels

This basalt knob near Coffee Lake is an erosional remnant of lava flows that once filled the valley between Sherwood and Tualatin

The Koller Wetland kolk pond in Tualatin

When the water was high enough it overtopped a divide separating the Tualatin Valley from the Willamette Valley. This happened near the I-5 freeway Boone Bridge over the Willamette River at Wilsonville. This new outlet allowed the water to speed up again and cut channels in what is now known as the Tonquin Geologic Area, also called the Tonquin Scablands and Tonquin Channels.

The Tonquin Scablands exhibit interwoven channels and divides, kolk lakes and ponds, erosional remnant basalt knobs, and gravel beds all of which illustrate the might of the water rushing from one valley to the next. Much of the area has been mined extensively for gravel and is not accessible by the public.

As the water kept filling the Tualatin Valley to almost 400 feet above sea level it found three low areas at the west end where it could flow into the Yamhill and Willamette Valleys.

At the same time the Yamhill Valley was overwhelmed from the northeast near Dayton by water flowing from the Tonquin channels and the Oregon City Channel converging with the water from these three west channels.

The two larger of these flood channels are the Yamhill Channel, flowing from the Tualatin Valley into the Yamhill Valley, and the Chehalem Channel flowing from the Tualatin Valley into the Willamette Valley.

The smaller of the three, the middle channel, only carried water for a short duration of about 80 feet deep when the water was at its highest level. Today Laughlin Road follows this route.

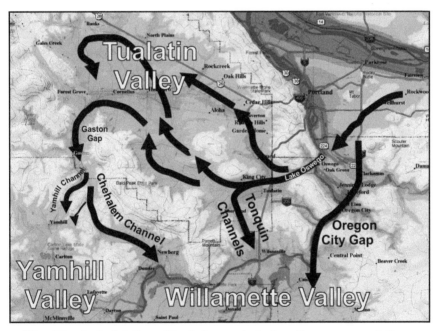

The Tualatin Valley filled through Lake Oswego and then flowed out through the Chehalem and Yamhill channels (left) and the Tonquin channels (center).

These three channels are much smaller than the Tonquin channels because less water flushed through them and had lost much of its energy. SR 47 West now traverses the furthest west (Yamhill Channel) between the towns of Gaston and Yamhill.

About two miles east is the larger Chehalem Channel with Chehalem Creek flowing through it. Where this channel funnels between hills on the north end there are giant current ripples caused by the 200 foot deep water rushing from the Tualatin into the Willamette Valley.

In the Fall of 2011, two large erratic boulders were identified on farmland near Gaston at the upper end of the Yamhill and Chehalem channels. On December 22, 2011 the 5,500 pound quartz-feldspar and 20,000 pound granite erratics joined several others already at the Tualatin Heritage Center where they are featured as part of the Tualatin Ice Age display.

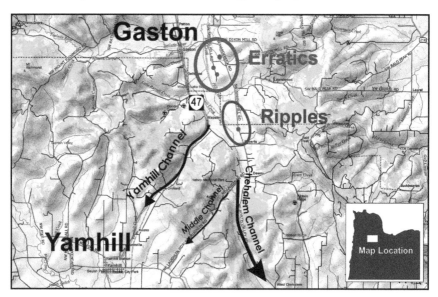

The Gaston Gap at the west end of the Tualatin Valley showing the Yamhill and Chehalem channels. Red circle indicates area where the Gaston erratics (red dots) were found. Green oval shows location of giant current ripples.

Looking north at the outflow area of the Chehalem Channel

Two very large erratic boulders delivered to the Tualatin Heritage Center in December, 2011

10 ton granite erratic found near Gaston now featured at the Tualatin Heritage Center in Tualatin

THIS 2.5 TON, QUARTZITE BOULDER IS AN
ICE AGE ERRATIC. IT WAS TRANSPORTED,
ENCASED IN AN ICEBERG, DURING ONE OF THE
CATACLYSMIC FLOODS THAT INUNDATED THIS
REGION OVER 15,000 YEARS AGO. IT ORIGINATED
NEAR MONTANA AND WAS DEPOSITED AT AN
ELEVATION OF 228 FEET NEAR GASTON, OREGON,
ABOUT 25 MILES WEST OF HERE.

A SPECIAL THANKS TO STELLA BRYANT,
BRIAN CLOPTON EXCAVATING INC. AND
AXIS CRANE

5,500 pound quartz-feldspar erratic at the Tualatin Heritage
Center

The Tualatin Heritage Center has a number of Tualatin's ice
age displays. The sacrum of a Harlan Ground Sloth, and the tusk
and molar of the mastodon, unearthed locally in 1962, are on
display at the Heritage Center. The other recovered parts of the
mastodon skeleton are on display at the Tualatin Public Library a
few blocks away.

Three large granite erratics were found just west of downtown
Tualatin and moved to Fields Bridge Park in West Linn. They
were not found on a hillside but on a fairly flat low area. Since the
three were found together they were most likely in the same
iceberg when it grounded.

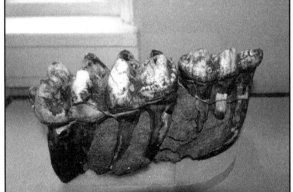

Partial
mastodon
skeleton in the
Tualatin Library;
molar and tusk
on
display at the
Tualatin
Heritage Center

48,000 pounds of granite erratics at Fields Bridge Park

Many of the erratics came to rest on hillsides, the perfect spot for an iceberg to be snagged and held firm until it melted and divested itself of whatever treasures it had captured on its way down the Purcell Trench in Idaho. But for these three to be stranded in a low spot might mean they arrived toward the end of the submersion of this valley when the flood was waning.

The Clackamas Community College erratic, moved from Tualatin to avoid destruction during the building of the I-205 freeway

Another traveling erratic is now holding court on the campus of Clackamas Community College in Oregon City with a brass plaque describing its provenance. It is the second largest found in western Oregon. This much rounder granite erratic came through Lake Oswego and grounded just southeast of the City of Tualatin.

As the GigaFlood rose, the whole Yamhill Valley acted as a conduit for waters entering from the north and exiting into the Willamette Valley to the south. This rising tide advanced through three channels west of Salem: the Salt Creek Channel, the Baskett Slough Channel and Holmes Gap, just four miles north of the town of Rickreall. Holmes Gap is the deepest of the three areas and shows evidence of the most erosion.

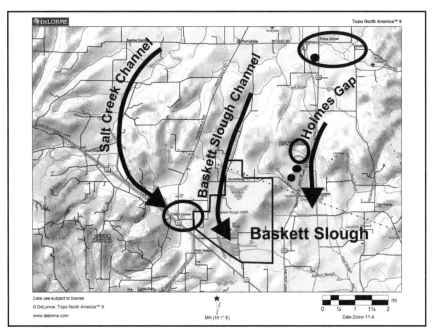

Lower end of the Yamhill Valley west of Salem The channels that allowed water to flow from the Yamhill Valley into the Willamette Valley. Ovals mark giant current ripples. Dots indicate locations where erratics have been found. Box delineates Baskett Slough National Wildlife Refuge.

Just south and west of Holmes Gap is the Baskett Slough National Wildlife Refuge. It is a permanent wetland no doubt formed, at least in part, by the GigaFlood.

Giant current ripples on Bethel Road near Perrydale; northwest of Salem

There are many glacial erratics and giant current ripples in this area, which shows it was a good catch basin for icebergs and that the water was still deep, fast-moving, and carrying a lot of soil.

The water flowing into the Willamette Valley from the Tualatin and Yamhill Valleys joined the water flowing down through the Oregon City Gap. The waters continued for 70 more miles south before halting near Eugene at the 400 foot elevation which was as high as it reached before turning around and flowing back north and out into the Pacific Ocean.

Chapter Fourteen
The Mad Rush for the Exits

A puzzle in doing ice age floods research in the Portland area was that it seemed to have flood channels going two opposite directions. It was answered in the discovery that the flood cut certain channels coming in and then different channels going out.

The influx of water through the Columbia River Gorge stopped almost as fast as it had begun. Then the - Gap stopped acting as a hydraulic dam and the water began to flow out faster than it was coming in. Just like turning off the faucet and opening the drain in the bathtub, the water started dropping throughout the entire Portland-Vancouver basin and the Tualatin, Yamhill, Clackamas and Willamette Valleys.

In the Clackamas River Valley, the water simply reversed directions and flowed west out through the Carver Gap. As it was exiting through the gap, the waters either formed or at least enlarged a receding waterfall near the Baker Cabin historic site.

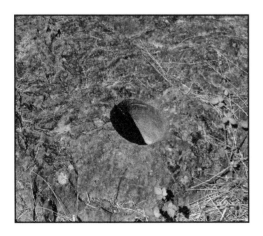

After the flood, the Clackamas River returned to its normal water volume and cut its present channel leaving the remains of the waterfall many feet above the present day water level.

Grinding hole close up

Grinding holes in water-worn bedrock behind the
Baker Cabin in Carver, Oregon

Today all that can be seen of the waterfall is an area of
exposed bedrock, which was used by the local Native Americans
as a grinding stone.

What started as potholes, in the ancient stream at the time of
the GigaFlood, were enlarged and used for preparing food.
Judging from the size and wear patterns it was utilized for many
years.

After the water exited the Carver Gap streaming west, it met
with the water flowing north exiting from the Willamette Valley.
These combined waters then turned northwest splitting into three
channels that are still visible today. A humongous whirlpool-like
action was formed as the waters flowing west and those flowing
north converged. The merging and diverging of the water caused a
vortex that left a large depression in the area of Clackamas Town
Center. This can be seen from I-205 as well as the undeveloped
flat meadow to the southeast occupied by some radio towers. This
area may become hard to discern as more and more development
fills it with buildings.

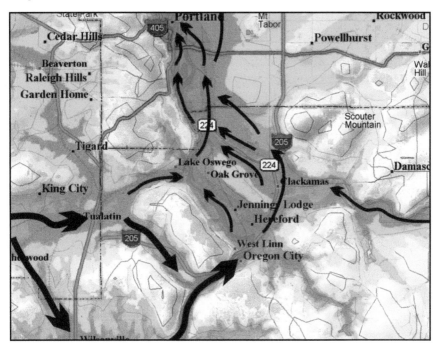

Exiting flood channels south of Portland

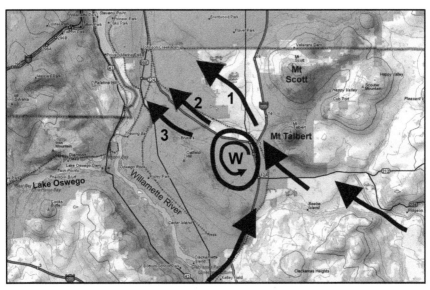

Clackamas Town Center whirlpool (W) and exit channels to
the northwest: (1) Johnson Creek, (2) Milwaukie
Expressway, and (3) Kellogg Creek.

This swirling water created the following three channels. The northernmost channel, has Johnson Creek Boulevard, Johnson Creek and the Springwater Corridor hiking trail following it. Traveling this channel provides some surprising views of the bluffs formed when the waters from the south swept northwestward to the Willamette River. The sediment was easily removed since it had just been deposited recently and was still saturated with water. This has left some distinct landslide features.

The easiest channel to see is the Milwaukie Expressway Channel (Highway 224). This is believed to be the ancestral bed of the Clackamas River before the GigaFlood diverted it. The deepest part of the channel is just to the north of the highway.

Kellogg Creek Channel is the southernmost of these channels. Kellogg Creek flows in it from Johnson City to Kellogg Lake abutting the Willamette River. With our current streets, this channel is more difficult to trace by car. But the west end is quite visible from McLoughlin Boulevard where Kellogg Lake empties into the Willamette River just two blocks south of SE Jefferson Street in Milwaukie, Oregon. Kellogg Lake is a kolk lake cut as the waters exited the Willamette Valley.

Kellogg Creek and Lake (center left) flow from southeast to northwest into the Willamette River. Elk Rock (in river on the right) is the top of an old volcano exposed by the cutting of the river channel by the draining of Lake Allison.

The water in the Tualatin Valley at first was able to exit through the Tonquin Channels and Lake Oswego; however, when the water dropped below about 150 feet both of these were denied. The huge amount of gravel dumped at Durham blocked the path through Lake Oswego. At Tonquin the water had never cut much deeper than about 150 feet. The remaining water had to find a new way out. This became the route of the Tualatin River that we know today and its tributaries Rock Creek and Fanno Creek.

As the Tualatin River was cutting this new channel, there seems to have been a slump off of Pete's Mountain to the south that required the river to go around the slide. It looks somewhat like a horseshoe. The water started eating away at the west end of the Willamette bar, on which the town of Willamette sits, as it followed the path of least resistance around the slide. Slumps like this one were caused by the ground being over-saturated with water and once the pressure was removed by the drop in the water level the heavy earth could not resist the pull of gravity.

Location of the Willamette Slump

All of the water from the Willamette Valley had to flow back out the narrow gap at Oregon City. Willamette Falls was formed by a receding waterfall as the water flowed out with tremendous force. In the same way that Niagara Falls or Dry Falls was formed, the tumultuous water undercut the lip of the falls causing it to recede upstream. It is thought that Willamette Falls started in line with the cliffs of West Linn and Oregon City and receded nearly 1.2 miles to its present location at Oregon City.

Willamette Falls from the air

Chapter Fifteen
The Water Departing Through Portland

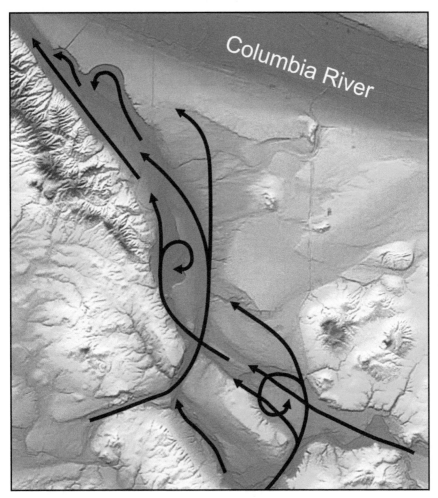

Lidar map of the Portland area showing the paths of the
GigaFlood as it rushed out to the Columbia River

Fast moving water does not make sharp turns, so after exiting the Oregon City Gap most of it continued in the same northeasterly direction until it was forced to turn by Mt. Talbert and Mt. Scott where it combined with the water coming out of the Clackamas River Valley, and formed the three channels already mentioned: Johnson Creek, Milwaukie Expressway and Kellogg Creek. (See map page 173)

Once the bulk of the incoming water made its way through the Columbia River Gorge, the water level in the Portland-Vancouver area began to drop as it flowed down the Columbia beyond the Kalama Gap. The water rushing north still had great force since it had the whole of Lake Allison, as far south as Eugene, pressing to be released. The beginning of this northward flow struck Alameda Ridge, which was deposited in the shadow of Rocky Butte, and sheared off the top of this gravel bar. That is why it is nearly flat. As the water dropped below the top surface of Alameda Ridge, the water's energy was concentrated and cut the channel where the Willamette River now flows and sculpted the lowland that is downtown Portland.

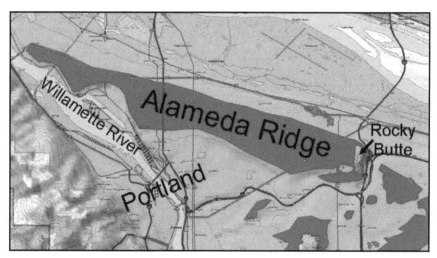

The 10.3 mile long Alameda Ridge gravel bar, once extending nearly 14 miles from Rocky Butte to the West Hills is now truncated at the west end by the Willamette River and almost cut in two by the out flowing floodwaters

The water almost cut another channel a little south of the end of the bar on the east side of the Willamette River. An eddy formed cutting a semi-circular cliff above Swan Island just south of where the University of Portland sits atop Mocks Crest. At one time those bluffs revealed rhythmites laid down as pulses of floodwater poured into the Portland basin. These are no longer visible due to buildings and vegetation.

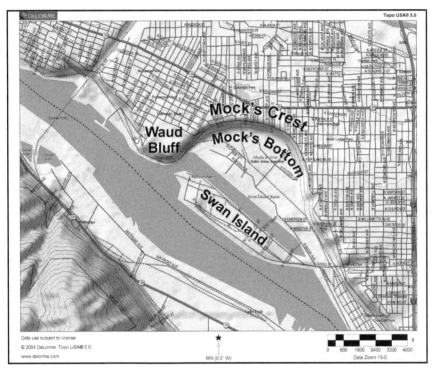

Topographic map of the Portland Bluffs and Swan Island. This 165 foot semi-circular cliff was cut into the ridge by the exiting flood

Geologists have thought that the straight edge of the east slope of the West Hills (Tualatin Mountains) was due entirely to an earthquake fault known as the West Hills Fault, but I personally think that the straight edge is possibly partly due to the shearing action of the exiting waters of the GigaFlood.

The Willamette River carried the floodwaters into the Columbia which flowed through Kalama Gap, and out to sea.

The Columbia Bar, where the river meets the Pacific Ocean, is one of the most dangerous crossings for ships entering a river due to the final deposition of debris from the GigaFlood. Instead of creating a delta the river forcefully jets out into the ocean. The sand bars are constantly being shifted by this force and it even creates standing waves in the river which collide with the ocean waves. It is no wonder the Columbia Bar, three miles wide and six miles long, has been called the "Graveyard of the Pacific" since approximately 2,000 large ships have sunk there.

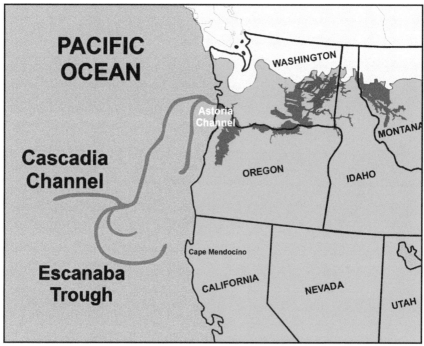

Distribution of Lake Missoula Flood sediments (brown)
in the Pacific Ocean

The Columbia River still carries much sand and silt today but the unfathomable amount carried to the ocean by the GigaFlood is revealed in it extensive dispersion. These sediments were deposited hundreds of miles west of today's shoreline and carried as far south as Cape Mendocino, California (400 miles south of the mouth of the Columbia River) by the ocean currents along the west coast of North America.

David Alt in his book, *Glacial Lake Missoula and its Humongous Floods*, said: "Urban development has obliterated most relics of the flood around Portland, and the few remaining are very hard to see. Lake Oswego is certainly the most spectacular souvenir of their passage. If present trends continue, it may soon be the only one easily visible."

He may be partially correct; however, I think we still have plenty to see now that we know where to look; what to look for and the increasing interest in the subject will spur further investigation of this region, revealing even more.

The evidence of the GigaFlood is all around us; has shaped our landscape, our commerce and our recreation and I hope this book has given you a greater appreciation of the uniqueness of this area.

Glossary

Andesite: Gray, fine-grained, volcanic rock generally midway in composition between basalt and rhyolite.

Anticline: A fold that bends layered rock up into an arch.

Argillite: A metamorphosed mud stone. Some erratics found in Oregon, including the Bellevue Erratic, are argillite.

Basalt: Volcanic rock caused by partial melting of the earth's crust. A common volcanic rock. Multiple basalt lava flows produced the Columbia Basin. It tends to break into palisades of vertical columns, which are easily eroded by fast flowing water. Most basalt is flat black, but that on the Columbia Basin weathers to a brownish black. Multiple layers are visible in the Columbia River Gorge and the Channeled Scablands of Washington.

Belt rocks: (Belt Supergroup) An enormous variety of distinctive sedimentary rock common to large areas of western Montana, northern Idaho, and southeastern British Columbia.

Capillary action: A complex action which occurs between a liquid and small openings in a solid. The liquid is actually drawn into or up into tiny capillaries. It is what allows a sponge to soak up water. In a glacier, water will use capillary action to tunnel through the solid ice just as water soaks through a cement wall of a basement.

Catastrophic principle or Catastrophism: A concept proposing that most major geological features on the earth's surface has been shaped by large catastrophes such as earthquakes, volcanism, tsunamis, asteroid hits, and floods rather than only slow gradual forces of erosion and deposition.

Cavitation: Erosion caused by water moving at least 100 feet per second (68 mph). This was one of the erosive forces during the Lake Missoula Flood for carving out flood channels.

Channeled Scablands: A term popularized by J Harlen Bretz, during the 1920's, to describe the areas in Washington state where the Lake Missoula Floods made channels in large, deep basalt flows.

Cobbles: A geologic term for a rock or rock fragment larger than a pebble and smaller than a boulder (Usually between 2.5 and 10.25 inches) and are often rounded.

Colonnade: The lower portion of a basalt flow consisting of large, well-formed clearly joined columns.

Composite volcano: Sometimes called stratovolcanoes. They are typically steep-sided, symmetrical cones of large dimension built of alternating layers of lava flows, volcanic ash, cinders, blocks, and bombs and may rise as much as 8,000 feet above their bases. The Cascade Mountains are composite volcanoes.

Cordilleran Ice Sheet: The glaciation which stretched across western North America from the Canadian Arctic.

Coulee: A water-cut valley, often with an elongated box-shape with steep sides and flat bottoms. Usually used in referring to the Lake Missoula Flood channels of eastern Washington.

Current ripple: See giant current ripple.

Debris flow: Rock, sand, mud and other material moved down slope by fast flowing water.

Delta: A delta is formed when a stream's velocity slows as it flows from a restricted area into an open plain, lake or sea.

Dike: A relatively thin sheet of igneous rock formed as molten magma filled a fracture.

Diorite: Coarsely granular igneous rock that consists mostly of plagioclase feldspar and pyroxene. Diorite superficially resembles granite but is darker and lacks quartz.

Discharge: The volume of water flowing through a stream.

Eddy bar: A sand or gravel bar that forms where eddy currents (swirling and reverse flows as in a whirlpool) develop along a flood route. Often found in the more protected mouths of tributaries.

Entablature: The upper portion of a basalt flow consisting of irregular, rough, jagged, hacky-like cooling fractures instead of columns.

Erosion and Deposition: The scientific terms for the natural removal and in-filling of earth materials.

Erosional Remnant: A topographic feature that remains above the general level to which erosion has reduced the surrounding landscape.

Erratic boulder: A rock somehow transported and dropped some distance from its source.

Exotic erratics: A rock foreign to where it is found. The Bellevue Erratic near McMinnville, Oregon is composed of argillite, which is only found in the area of northern Idaho, western Montana and Canada.

Fault: A vertical or diagonal fracture in the earth's crust along which the rocks have moved.

Flood channel: A path cut by floodwaters, generally having a box shape, which may or may not contain flowing water at this time.

Flood shadow: Areas blocked from the affects of the flood by an obstacle such as Prune Hill or Rocky Butte.

Foreset beds: A series of inclined symmetrically arranged layers of a cross-bedding unit formed by deposition of sediments that rolled down a steep frontal slope of a delta or dune or gravel bar.

Gaps: See water gaps.

Geologist: A person who studies geology.

Geology: The scientific study of the structure of the earth and the forces that shaped it. There are two types: 1) operational which uses the scientific method of observation and repeatable testing, and 2) historical which has to draw conclusions just based on the evidence with no way to test the hypotheses because we cannot repeat the past.

Geomorphology: The study of the changes in landforms due to volcanoes, earthquakes, weather, floods, etc. A "fluvial-geomorphologist" concentrates on earth changes made by water.

Giant current ripples: Similar to ripples on a beach, but much larger, these are waves of sand and gravel deposited by deep, fast moving flood currents. The giant ripples of the Lake Missoula floods and the scablands are as much as 35 feet high and several hundred feet from crest to crest indicating enormous speeds and depths of water.

Glacial erratics: Rocks transported on or in glaciers and icebergs. Approximately 400 have been cataloged in the Willamette Valley. Also called "Iceberg Erratics" when found in areas that were never glaciated, but were inundated by icebergs carried by floods.

Glacial lakes: Lakes formed by the impounding of waters behind a glacier or ice lobe, such as Lake Missoula and Lake Columbia.

Glacial moraine: The debris pushed in front (terminal moraine) or sloughed off the sides (lateral moraines) of a glacier. It is composed of unsorted gravels, dirt and clay, and large and small boulders. Ice lobes may also have moraines.

Glacier-outburst floods: (Jökulhlaups) Outburst floods from rapidly melting glaciers. Outburst floods become debris flows by incorporating large quantities of sediment from valley floors and walls, often by triggering landslides that mix with the floodwaters. The debris is stratified as if laid down over time but also unsorted as if laid down rapidly.

Granite: A coarse-grained intrusive igneous rock that consists mostly of feldspar and quartz. Most granites also contain black biotite. Many of the erratics found in Oregon are granite.

Gravel pit: A place where rock and gravel are removed without the need for blasting.

Gulch filling: A deposit of sand and gravel swept into the slack water of a small tributary valley by a flood down the main valley.

Hanging Valley: A tributary valley that joins a main valley where the latter has been deepened, usually by erosion, resulting in a steep drop from the floor of the tributary valley to the floor of the main valley.

Headward erosion: Stream erosion starting downstream and cutting a larger channel upstream toward the source of the water.

Hydraulic dam: A land constriction where the icebergs and other flood debris contribute to the restriction and impounding of the water which is coming in faster on the upstream side than is being released on the downstream side.

Ice Age: A period in earth's history when over 30% of the earth was covered with ice sheets and glaciers.

Ice dam: A blockage made of ice stopping normal stream drainage.

Iceberg erratics: See Ice-rafted boulders

Ice lobe: A finger of ice pushed out from an ice sheet by the weight of ice in the center of the sheet. The Puget and Purcell Lobes are examples.

Ice-rafted boulders: Iceberg transported rocks, of a foreign material, found in an area known not to have been glaciated in the past.

Ice Sheet: An ice field covering a large area (more than 50,000 square kilometers) also known as a continental glacier. Today there are two ice sheets: Antarctica and Greenland. During the last glacial maximum the Cordilleran and Laurentide Ice Sheets covered much of Canada and parts of North America.

Igneous rock: Rock formed by the cooling of lava either above (extrusive) or below the earth's surface (intrusive).

Jökulhlaups: See glacier-outburst floods.

Kolk: An extremely strong vortex that swirls around a more or less vertical axis in deep, very fast, flowing water. Kolks are capable of plucking large boulders out of solid bedrock.

Kolk lake or kolk pond: Depressions left in a flood channel, often filled with water.

Landslides: A wide range of ground movement, such as rock falls, deep failure of slopes or shallow debris flows. A slump is a landslide often caused by over-saturated earth.

Lava: Extrusive igneous rock that has erupted in a molten state onto the earth's surface.

Lidar: Light Detection and Ranging. A remote sensing method that uses light in the form of a pulsed laser to measure ranges (variable distances) to the earth.

Loess: Soil made up of fine sand particles and silt. (See: Palouse silt)

Metamorphosed rock: Igneous or sedimentary rock that has been changed by heat and/or pressure.

Moraine: See glacial moraine.

Mudstone: A sedimentary rock formed from mud.

Palagonite: A yellowish alteration product that forms through reaction of basalt with steam, commonly where basalt lava flows entered water.

Palouse Hills: The rolling countryside composed of windblown dust in eastern Washington and western Idaho.

Palouse silt: A deep and richly fertile deposit of windblown dust (called loess by geologists) that covers much of eastern Washington and western Idaho.

Pea gravel: Small, smooth, rounded stones consisting of pieces the size of peas.

Pillow lava: A cylindrical mass of basalt that forms where lava flows moved under water. Common in the oceanic crust, and locally in the Pacific Northwest.

Plunge pool: A deep circular hole eroded at the base of a waterfall by the force of the water plunging over the falls or cataract.

Pothole: A hole generally deeper than wide, worn into the solid rock at falls and strong rapids by sand, gravel, or stones being spun in a circular motion by the force of the current.

Precipitation: Any or all of the forms of water particles, whether liquid or solid, that fall from clouds and reach the ground.

Quarry: A mining operation where rock is removed with blasting and other removal techniques.

Receding waterfall: This is formed as the forwarding flow tumbling over an edge undercuts the lip of the falls and it recedes.

Rock flour: Finely ground rock which was pulverized as rocks scraped against each other and with surface rocks in a moving glacier.

Rhythmite: Layers of sediment laid down in water in a rhythmical pattern, usually coarse on the bottom and fine at the top.

Sand bar: A ridge of sedimentary sand that has been deposited in the middle or along the banks of a stream by a decrease in stream velocity.

Scabland: A term geologists use to describe areas where soil has been scraped away, exposing irregular areas of the underlying basalt. A tract of land that is unfit for farming because it is scarred with dry stream channels, full of rock outcroppings, or covered with coarse gravel.

Sedimentary rocks: Rocks formed from deposits of erosional material such as gravel, sand, mud, silt, or clay. Most sedimentary rocks are layered.

Silt: Sediment finer than sand, coarser than clay.

Slumps: Landslides in which the shifting material moves in a block. Many slumps were caused by the ice age floods, especially as the water level lowered leaving over-saturated hillsides.

Strand line: Horizontal line, etched by wave action from a standing body of water, across hillsides that mark the shoreline of ancient lakes.

Striations: Scrape marks left on glacial erratics and bedrock caused by rocks being dragged along during glacial movements.

Syncline: A fold in layered rocks that are bent downward into a trough.

Talus: The rock debris that weathers from a cliff or escarpment. When this debris falls to the base of the cliff and piles up at an angle it is called a talus slope.

Terrain: Area of the earth's surface with a distinctive geological character.

Topographic profile: A cross-sectional view along a line drawn through a portion of a topographic map.

Topographic map: A two-dimensional map representing three-dimensional relief, using contour lines and shadows.

Topography: The study of earth's surface features.

Troutdale Formation: Coarse gravel and sand deposited in the Portland-Vancouver basin and many places in the Cascade anticline. Generally recognized by high-energy, embricated sediments naturally cemented together containing a high percentage of quartzites and other rocks from the northern Rocky Mountains.

Truncated hills: Hills that have been cut off by some force such as glaciers or floods. Characterized by at least one straight side that appears contrary to natural erosion.

Underfit stream: A stream that is much smaller than the valley it occupies.

Uniformitarian Principle or Uniformitarianism: A concept proposing that all geological features were formed by slow processes of erosion and deposition just as we observe today. Sudden events like volcanoes, earthquakes, floods and asteroid hits are not considered when describing how most major features are formed.

Varves: Alternating thin layers of pale silt and darker clay deposited in layers in lakes. These are sometimes thought to be annual layers of winter and summer deposits but can also be formed by surges of water as from a melting glacier.

Venturi effect: The phenomenon that water moving through a narrow channel will move faster than the same amount of water moving through a wider channel.

Vesicular lava: Frothy lava filled with holes from expanding gas bubbles that has risen to the top of the flow.

Water gap: A deep pass in a mountain ridge, through which a stream flows; especially a narrow gorge or ravine cut through resistant rocks often when there appears to have been an easier route around the barrier.

Wind gap: A pass through a mountain ridge that has no water flowing through it.

Selected Bibliography

Allen, John Eliot. *The Magnificent Gateway: A Layman's Guide to the Geology of the Columbia River Gorge.* Forest Grove, Oregon, Timber Press, 1979.

Allen, John Eliot and Majorie Burns with Sam C. Sargent. *Cataclysms on the Columbia.* Portland, Oregon, Timber Press, 1986.

Allen, John Eliot and Majorie Burns and Scott Burns. *Cataclysms on the Columbia: The Great Missoula Floods.* Portland, Oregon, Ooligan Press, Portland State University 2009.

Alt, David. *Glacial Lake Missoula and Its Humongous Floods.* Missoula, Montana, Mountain Press, 2003.

Alt, David and Donald W. Hyndman. *Northwest Exposures: A Geologic Story of the Northwest.* Missoula, Montana, Mountain Press, 1995.

Alt, David and Donald W. Hyndman. *Roadside Geology of Idaho.* Missoula, Montana, Mountain Press Publishing Company, 1989.

Alt, David and Donald W. Hyndman. *Roadside Geology of Montana.* Missoula, Montana, Mountain Press Publishing Company, 2001.

Alt, David and Donald W. Hyndman. *Roadside Geology of Oregon.* Missoula, Montana, Mountain Press Publishing Company, 1981.

Alt, David and Donald W. Hyndman. *Roadside Geology of Washington.* Missoula, Montana, Mountain Press Publishing Company, 1984.

Bjornstad, Bruce. *On the Trail of the Ice Age Floods: A geological field guide to the Mid-Columbia Basin.* Sandpoint, Idaho, Keokee Press, 2006.

Bjornstad, Bruce and Eugene Kiver. *On the Trail of the Ice Age Floods The Northern Reaches: A geological field guide to northern Idaho and the Channeled Scabland.* Sandpoint, Idaho, Keokee Press, 2012.

Carson, Robert J. and Michael E. Denny, et al. *Where the Great River Bends: A natural and human history of the Columbia at Wallula.* Sandpoint, Idaho, Keokee Press, 2009.

Friedman, Ralph. *Oregon for the Curious.* Caldwell, Idaho, Caxton Printers, Ltd., 1972.

Ice Age Flood: Catastrophic Transformation of the West. VHS. Seattle, Washington, Northwest Interpretive Association; Portland, Oregon, Oregon Public Broadcasting, 28 min.

Jones & Jones. *Ice Age Floods Alternatives Study: A Park Without Boundaries.* Funded by the National Park Service through its Special Resource Study Program, 2000.

Lidar Data and Lidar Imagery Series Publication. Oregon Department of Geology and Mineral Industries, Portland, Oregon.

Manske, Ken. *A Traveler's Guide to The Historic Columbia River Highway.* Gresham, Oregon, M&A Tour Books.

Mueller, Marge and Ted. *Fire, Faults, and Floods: A Road and Trail Guide Exploring the Origins of the Columbia River Basin.* Moscow Idaho, University of Idaho Press, 2001.

Mystery of the Megaflood: Examining the World's Most Catastrophic Flood. WGBH, Boston, Nova Program, 2005, 56 min.

Oard, Michael. *The Missoula Flood Controversy and the Genesis Flood*. Creation Research Society, 2004.

Plummer, Charles C. and David McGeary and Diane H. Carlson. *Physical Geology*. McGraw-Hill, 1999.

Really, Really Big Floods. VHS. KUFM Public Television, 2002, 28 min.

Sculpted by Floods: The Northwest's Ice Age Legacy. VHS. KSPS-TV, Spokane, 2001, 57 min.

Soennichsen, John. *Bretz's Flood: The Remarkable Story of a Rebel Geologist and the World's Greatest Flood*. Seattle, Washington. Sasquatch Books, 2008.

Soennichsen, John. *Washington's Channeled Scablands Guide: Explore and Recreate along the Ice Age Floods National Geologic Trail*. Seattle, Washington, The Mountaineers Books, 2012.

The Great Floods: Cataclysms of the Ice Age. VHS. Washington State University in cooperation with Coulee Dam National Recreation Area, National Park Service.

Weis, Paul and William L. Newman. *The Channeled Scablands of Eastern Washington: The Geologic Story of the Spokane Flood*. Cheney Washington, Eastern Washington University Press, 1999.

Williams, Ira A. *Geologic History of the Columbia River Gorge: as interpreted from the historic Columbia River Scenic Highway*. Portland, Oregon, Oregon Historical Society Press, 1991.

Index

S

Saddle Mountains, 67
Salmon Creek Channel, 101, 102, 114, 119
Salt Creek Channel, 169
Sandy River, 115-116, 118
Sandy River Valley, 117-118
Sauvie Island, 100-101, 114, 119
Scouter Mountain, 131
Seismic Theory, 61
Selkirk Mountains, 30
Sentinel Gap, 45, 56, 67-68, 70, 87
Shellrock Mountain, 96
Snake River, 54, 58, 69
Spokane Flood, 36, 87
Spring Gulch, 71
Springwater Corridor, 131, 174
Strandlines, 26-27, 68
Sullivan's Gulch, 129-132
Swan Island, 179
Swan Range, 33

T

Tebo Pit, 112
Tom McCall Nature Preserve, 79, 80
Tonquin Channel, 160-164, 175
Tonquin Geologic Area, 162
Tonquin Scablands, 160, 162
Toutle River, 118
Troutdale Formation, 103
Tualatin Heritage Center, 164-167
Tualatin Library, 166-167
Tualatin Mountains (see West Hills)
Tualatin River, 9, 136, 147, 157, 175
Tualatin Valley, 84, 133, 155-156, 158, 160, 162-164, 170
Tualatin-Willamette Channel, 136
Turbidity flow, 89
Twin Sisters, 34, 70

Other items available from Rick Thompson at: www.GigaFlood.com

The World's Most Beautiful Highway Booklet
The the story of why Sam Lancaster succeeded in the building the old Columbia Gorge Highway when others had failed.

The Hunt for Iceberg Erratics
A 32-page full-color book, 81 photographs, 17 locations (with maps and GPS), telling how to identify erratics, types of erratics, and a page for your own discoveries.

Self-guided driving tours
See the evidence of the
Lake Missoula Floods in:
     Clark County
     Clackamas County
     Columbia River Gorge
       Oregon & Washington sides
     Portland/Vancouver
     Tualatin/Sherwood
     Willamette Valley

Each guide has: map in the center, detailed driving directions, and describes flood features en route.

Find these and much more at: **www.GigaFlood.com**

CPSIA information can be obtained
at www.ICGtesting.com
Printed in the USA
LVHW07s1342100818
586614LV00027B/855/P